FERTILE GROUND

SPENSER BRASSARD

FERTILE GROUND

A **MIND-BODY** APPROACH TO **GETTING PREGNANT** WITHOUT IT TAKING OVER **YOUR LIFE**

HOUNDSTOOTH PRESS

FERTILE GROUND
*A Mind-Body Approach to Getting Pregnant
without It Taking over Your Life*

FIRST EDITION

ISBN   978-1-5445-4567-7   *Hardcover*
       978-1-5445-4566-0   *Paperback*
       978-1-5445-4568-4   *Ebook*

For every woman who has ever felt the deep desire to be a mama.

CONTENTS

LISTEN TO THIS PLAYLIST *WHILE* YOU READ

I created this playlist for you to listen to while you read. I listened to it while I wrote the book, and it made for a much more emotionally felt experience. My hope is to gift you this embodied experience too. Search "Fertile Ground Book" on Spotify to tune in.

INTRODUCTION

I'm not your typical fertility expert. Nor did I set out to study the field of fertility. And this isn't your ordinary fertility book. I won't put you on a restrictive meal plan and prohibit you from eating pizza. I won't demand you take countless supplements with ingredients you can't pronounce. I'm not interested in reviewing your lab work with a fine-toothed comb and then insisting you do more tests to figure out "what's wrong with you." I went through that whole circus myself for eight years, and I know how exhausting and demoralizing it can be. I'm here to propose a different approach to increasing your fertility *without it taking over your life*. It's a process that is gentler, kinder, more compassionate toward yourself, and far more effective.

I'm imagining you right now as a weary traveler.

Like me, you've been on a complex and confusing road. While most women seem able to conceive babies easily and without strain, your path has been windy and unruly.

Although at times, your hope has wavered, you haven't given up. You still feel the call in your heart to create your baby. And this deep, powerful, primal wanting has brought you...to this book.

I'm imagining you standing outside as you try to find your way. I'm opening the door and inviting you to come inside. Step through the door. Join me. Curl up in a comfy chair. Let's get you a warm drink. Let's spend time together by the fire. And let's explore a different approach to your baby.

Take a moment to simply arrive within this moment. Take off your shoes. Wrap yourself in a blanket. Notice where you're seated. Feel the weight of this book in your hands. Take a breath.

You have arrived. The old journey is ending. Another is beginning. Now, your journey is moving away from struggle, grinding, and hustle and toward a feeling of relief. Something new is being born. Can you feel it?

As you arrive, I want you to know that getting pregnant doesn't have to feel unbearable. *There is another way.* To set this new adventure in motion, I want you to know these three important things:

1. There is a highly overlooked piece to the fertility puzzle: *the mind and body connection.*

Although you might feel like you're the only woman in the world who can't yet get pregnant, at the time I am writing this book, one in six are currently experiencing fertility struggles, according to the World Health Organization.[1] These struggles illustrate a dire need for high-quality care and solutions.

And, despite the cultural belief that fertility struggles are purely a physical issue, they are not. Your mind, your thoughts, and your emotions influence your physiology.

The mind and body create a dynamic dance. What's happening in your body can impact your mental state. Conversely, your thoughts and emotions wield a profound influence on your body's functions. For example, emotions trigger hormonal responses that affect heart rate, blood pressure, immune system activity, and reproductive health.

Mind and body are designed to be partners, working together to bring you happiness and health, which *includes a gorgeous baby.* This book will provide real-life stories, simple tools, and solid research to support this.

Maybe you're asking, "If my mind can supposedly influence my chances of getting pregnant, then why hasn't my doctor said anything about this?" Well, your OB-GYN or reproductive endocrinologist is trained to treat your body exclusively, not your brain, heart, or spirit.

Does this mean your fertility journey is "all your fault" because you haven't harnessed the power of the mind–body connection? Absolutely not. (I will continue to make this very clear throughout the book.) You can't possibly expect to do something you've never learned. We exist in a world that lives primarily from the neck up. We are burdened and distracted by the endless, racing thoughts in our brains. We overvalue and overanalyze life's problems with tired minds and we genuinely have no idea how to connect with or process our life experiences inside our bodies that lead to more excellent mental and physical health.

As a culture, we are highly disconnected from the natural process and intelligence of our bodies.

This can stand in the way of optimal fertility because when you learn how to connect your mind and body, it elicits an ideal relaxation response for peace of mind and hormonal balance, which increases your chances of conception.

2. Stressing less is easier said than done.

I tried to conceive for almost a decade. I landed on numerous online forums titled "Ten ways to get pregnant fast!" Every single one required nine different chores I could do to support my physical health, and then the tenth item on the list would be to "stress less."

Asking someone to stress less without tools or guidance to do it is like expecting a plant to grow without water or sunlight. Like a lack of nourishment, stress can stunt personal growth and well-being. Just as plants need specific care to thrive, individuals need tailored strategies and support to respond to stress and flourish.

There's this study of couples who had insurance coverage for three IVF (in vitro fertilization) cycles, did not conceive, and did not return for a third treatment cycle.[2] As a follow-up, they were asked to complete a survey giving reasons for not returning. The vast majority said it was due to stress.

"I had had enough," "emotional cost," and "could not cope with treatment" were some of their valid responses. Even though treatment was financially free, the mental price was still too much to bear.

Not only can the ups and downs of the journey be tough to cope with emotionally (particularly without mind–body tools), but most of us find proof in our utter exhaustion that stress is obviously hard on the body and makes life feel exceedingly chaotic.

Your desire, better yet, *your basic need* for fresh perspectives and tools to support your health throughout your fertility journey (and your life), is so incredibly valid.

Finally, here's a surprising twist to the fertility puzzle...

3. **This fertility journey isn't just about having a baby.**

There's more purpose to it than that.

It's about un-becoming who you think you *should* be so you can be who you really are.

It's about blooming into the woman and mother you're meant to be (and feeling the relief of this) even before your baby arrives.

It's about embodying a womanhood that breathes both stability and empowerment. Unafraid to voice her needs, she is a woman who releases herself from unrealistic, perfectionist standards. She treasures her body as a loyal companion throughout life. She navigates uncertainty with trust that life is working in her favor. She surrenders to a greater purpose.

Are you willing to give birth twice? To a beautiful new version of you and a beautiful child?

Your fertility journey is an opportunity to create two extraordinary new lives: yours and your baby's. It's a journey of self-discovery (or it can be, if you allow it). And, on this wild and emotionally challenging journey, you need a loving, powerful guide. Someone to offer guidance, inspiration, and reassurance. That's why each chapter in this book is a Message from Fertility.

If Fertility were a real-life person, what messages would she have for you? She would be unhurried, leisurely, never rushing, yet always right on time. She's never behind or late. Time expands for her. Good things are drawn to her. By doing less, she creates more. She's curious to hear what your physician recommends, and she has her own suggestions too. As you read this book, I hope you'll experience a moment—even if it's only one breath, in and out, or one second—where you connect with the energy of Fertility and feel it within all the cells in your body.

Mostly, though, this book is my love letter to you.

I see you and refer to you already as a "Mama Bear" who is fiercely determined. The woman who is doing everything in her power to get pregnant finally. The woman sacrificing everything she has—money, time, and energy—to make this baby. She might be so confused about what to do next. She has had her heart broken so many times and doesn't know who to trust. She hides in the corner of family gatherings and is a shell of who she used to be. Our culture has wrongfully conditioned her to believe that hard work, hustling, and depriving herself of everything she enjoys is how to get what she wants. But it doesn't have to be that way anymore.

This book contains my story, and dozens of fertility stories from my generous clients. These stories are here to comfort you, remind you that you're not alone, and reveal another way to your baby. It's a way back to your authentic self.

You can hold two things at once. One, a desire to hold a child in your arms. Two, the recognition that your life is good, sweet, and filled with reasons to be quite grateful right now. You can enjoy your life now as it is while simultaneously wanting more. Both/and. Dancing in this duality not only makes life a helluva lot more fun, but also lowers your stress levels, increases your fertility, and makes it easier for you and your baby to find each other.

MY PROFESSIONAL CREDENTIALS

I specialize in mind–body medicine as a path to find peace now and boost your fertility. After twelve years of studying the field of fertility, I'm proud to report that 70 percent of my clients get pregnant within one year after working with me, and this is typically after years of fertility struggles. The 30 percent of those who don't get pregnant (yet) transform in beautiful ways too. They're living their lives again, enjoying vacations and date nights with their partners (without discussions about babies or fertility), and feeling more confident to take up space in our world regardless of their pregnancy status. They don't have to control everything anymore. They're safe to be who they are and feel how they feel.

WHAT'S DIFFERENT NOW...BESIDES THE BABY?

I asked a few clients, "Since working with me, what has changed for you...besides having a baby?" Women shared their thoughts:

"I took a day off work not because I was sick, but simply because I needed rest."

"Silenced my phone so I don't get pestered by constant notifications."

"Sex is so damn good!"

"Reduced my work hours overall and have more space for my personal life."

"I asked for a raise!"

"I love sleeping in on weekends."

"I stopped fighting myself. If I'm sad, I feel it. I meet myself where I'm at."

"I took a Jet Ski ride and felt like a kid again!"

"Enjoying pizza with real cheese and sparkling wine."

"I've grieved and healed from pregnancy loss and feel lighter than before."

"I no longer try to force my goals to happen. I'm still ambitious, but there's a softer feeling now. I allow good things to come to me rather than chasing. Ironically, this has made me even more successful."

"I feel more calm no matter how my journey unfolds. Whether I get pregnant naturally, through IVF, a donor cycle, adoption, or some other way, I'm surrendering to the mystery. I recognize I can influence the outcome, but it's not entirely in my control. Knowing this brings me so much peace."

"I have a greater appreciation for my life right now, even if nothing changes."

"I'm learning to mother and love myself as much as I long to mother and love my future baby."

These experiences are waiting for you, Mama Bear, as you shift your fertility journey from what it has been...to something new.

MY POINT OF VIEW

Every fertility expert has their point of view. Here is mine:

There are infinite paths to your perfect, healthy baby.

You can conceive naturally. Or you might use some support from modern medicine, whether IVF or another option. There is no right or wrong way, no better or worse way, no good or bad way. It will be the same precious baby in the end.

Choose the path that feels right and true to *you*. No one else. Ultimately, the goal is for *your* mind and body to feel safe and at peace and to feel at home.

One thing's for sure: no matter how it happens, you'll want to quiet the rushing thoughts in your mind, feel at ease in your body, and connect to a higher plan and higher purpose that knows the way.

There are universal truths in every fertility journey.

Your fertility journey is unique. Nobody on earth is going through the same experience as you. The path to your baby, the doors you're meant to walk through, and the particular experiences are unique to you. No one can duplicate it, and you can't copy and paste another couple's journey to your success.

At the same time, you will find universal truths in every fertility journey. As women, we're more alike than we are different. We can see solace in each others' stories as we realize, "Thank God. I thought it was just me. I'm not the only one."

"BUT MY STORY IS SPECIAL!"

"Spenser, I'm forty-four, so I don't think mind–body medicine will work for me..."

"I have a rare medical condition, so I don't think what you're saying applies to someone like me..."

"The thing is, there's a history of fertility struggles in my family, so..."

I've worked with many women who believed that their age, diagnosis, treatment history, or personal fertility story makes them "special" and therefore exempt from the strategies I teach. Many women think, *This stuff may work for other women, but it won't work for me. I'm different.*

Here's my response: Is it possible you're dealing with certain things that might be considered rare or unusual compared to the average person? Yes. (I can relate. I have two uteruses. How's *that* for different?)

However, the beauty of mind–body medicine is that it does not discriminate.

Mind–body medicine has the ingredients that every TTC (trying to conceive) woman needs, regardless of her unique factors. Just like every newborn baby needs nourishment and care, every woman does too.

Your monkey mind (your busy, overactive, chattering brain) is clever in attempting to keep distance between you and the success stories you're about to read. Observe how it does this as you read this book. And then, decide that you're ready and able to let that story of "specialness" go simply by having more awareness of it.

The stories from the women in this book include many different diagnoses from their doctors—and a few are from women in their forties.

THE FERTILITY JOURNEY: A LESSON ON SELF-TRUST

Despite what the fertility industry and the fear-mongering forums of the internet have proclaimed to you, please know this: *You are the only one who holds the compass to your baby.*

I know you want the Google Maps breakdown of how and when you'll arrive at your destination. But all you need to know is the next right step, according to what *you* want, need, and crave.

Initially, it feels a bit backward for women to believe the fertility journey can be this enlivening and that trusting yourself, doing what you want to do, and allowing yourself to feel how you actually feel increases fertility. We have been manipulated into believing it doesn't matter how we feel and to push past the burnout of our nervous systems.

As you read this book, notice bits and pieces that make your whole body soften and sit back in your chair. Peel back the corners of pages that help you become aware of the clues inside the stories that instinctively make your body take a deep sigh of relief. Take note and highlight each sentence that fills you with the relief and answers you've been praying for. Then come back to these sections again and again until your body has registered it as your new truth and, eventually, a new reality.

MORE THAN ANYTHING ELSE...

There is one important message I received via download from the Universe when I was on my journey, and every time I share it with my clients, I see their whole being loosened into the present moment.

There is no rush.

There is no rush to read this book. There is no rush to strengthen your mind–body connection. There is no rush even to enjoy your life. It will all unfold organically and without force. Let it do the work on you.

If there's one story that illustrates Fertility's transformation and time-bending energy, it's Cammie's. Her story shows how dramatically your life changes when you stop rushing to the finish line and approach your fertility journey differently. I can think of no better story to kick off this book.

I hope this woman's story plants a tiny seed in your mind: "I don't have to rush. By slowing down to meet myself, I will meet my baby."

CAMMIE'S STORY

I was four miscarriages into my fertility journey and grieving my mother's passing.

After releasing her from the earth, I was handling all the business affairs of her death. And I was thrust into complicated dynamics with family members—people whom I had long since chosen to love from a distance.

I was a wreck inside, tender to the touch with pain and heartache, and wearing the finest chain-link armor. My motto was, "If you stay ready, you don't have to get ready." I was ready for war. I imagine my armor as the most fabulous of garments, golden and gleaming, intricate designs on the breastplate and jewel encrusted. I looked good. I was poised and high functioning. But the armor, as armor does, kept my movements hindered and blocked me from receiving goodness and harm.

To this day, I cannot recall how I discovered Spenser and her work around fertility. I assume it was some sort of rabbit hole of connections made by my unceasing and insatiable need to get and stay pregnant. Somehow, I found her website and scheduled a call.

We talked about my miscarriages, my pain, and my confusion. I remember Spenser telling me, "We can work on your fertility if you want to. But we can also set that topic aside and work on healing your heart."

I was so relieved to hear her say this. I hadn't known it going into the call, but when I heard her say we didn't necessarily have to talk about fertility or baby-making, I felt such relief. My shoulders relaxed, my abdomen softened, and I took a deep breath in and out.

I realized, "I still want to be a mother. I don't want to give up on my dream yet. But what I really need right now is to focus on myself. I need to choose myself and bring attention to healing and opening my heart instead of shutting down. What's up for me right now is more than the need for a baby." My emotional and mental health needs to be prioritized above anything else.

Spenser helped me to see that healing my heart was not only a worthwhile endeavor for my own peace and well-being, but it was also the pathway through which my motherhood would be discovered.

Making the choice to choose myself, I loosened the white-knuckle grip I had on the need to get pregnant. Leading up to this point, I had been obsessed with tracking my menstrual cycle and ovulation, taking all the supplements, drinking all the teas and herbs, and soaking my feet every night to keep my body temperature up. I created the whole circus, trying to make my body do what I thought it was too broken to do. When I freed myself from all of this, I looked around and saw one heck of an amazing life.

I saw a beautiful hunk of a husband who loved me and had been by my side, sitting ringside at the circus. A man who held my hand and cleaned me up after every devastating loss we had been through. I saw a beautiful home and all the comforts I always dreamed of. I saw a network of family and friends who loved me and enjoyed my presence. So much to be grateful for. It was there all along, but I had been too preoccupied to see it.

I don't have a baby yet. That is true. I have a splendid life. That is also true. Both can be true at the same time.

It was humbling to realize, "I've been seeing myself as a victim." Without being conscious, I had sunk into the belief that the world is a cold and hostile place, that dreams rarely work out, that suffering is inevitable, and that everything is unfair. This victim mentality stripped the joy from my life.

In March 2019, I broke my contract with victimhood. To commemorate this shift, I planned a luxurious vacation. "Let's go celebrate the gift of life!" I told my husband. By May 2019, I was pregnant.

We scheduled our vacation for July 2019. I imagined drinking tequila on the beach and living la vida loca! Instead, I ate a humble breakfast each morning before the wave of nausea set in for the day, laid in a beach cabana poolside everyday, feeling like a beached whale, and sipped coconut water. It was a beautiful vacation, although not the one I originally envisioned!

My son is now three and a half years old. I cry when I think about how magical and mysterious life is.

To the woman reading these words: no matter what is showing up for you right now, no matter what you've been through, I promise that if you choose yourself, you will not regret it. If you choose to search for yourself with half as much vigor as you are searching for the right recipe to make your baby, you will find what you are looking for. I wish you the courage to witness just how good your life is right now.

MY FERTILITY STORY

ONCE UPON A TIME...

For as long as I can remember, I wanted to be a mom more than anything in the world. At age ten, I would pretend to be sick so I could stay home from school and watch TLC's *A Baby Story*. I wasn't interested in Barbie, the grown-up doll with her dream house, car, and career. I wanted baby dolls so I could play "mommy." Even in my adolescent years, when I loved partying and being free as a bird, I couldn't wait to settle down and start a family.

I come from a long line of stay-at-home moms with big, noisy, chaotic houses. I was one of four siblings, and our home was in a state of pandemonium all the time. Kids ran around everywhere, putting on musical performances, jumping on couches, and building forts. Hockey sticks were scattered in the foyer, and screams echoed in the halls. My mother drank an entire pot of coffee every day, even though it triggered her migraines, just to summon enough energy to handle her offspring. Even though she seemed exhausted at times, her heart was enormous; she adored her kids, and I wanted to follow in her footsteps.

From watching her, my sister, my grandmother, and the other matriarchs in my family, I learned that being a mom is the most important thing a woman can do with her body and her life. There was never any question. *I wanted to be a mama.*

I met the love of my life at seventeen, married at twenty-two, then waited a year or so before trying to conceive so I wouldn't seem "too desperate." (Joke's on me.) We were off on the baby-making train! One-way ticket to kidsville! My husband would agree that right off the bat, our journey felt stressful. There was already so much pressure to make it happen. I was so attached to becoming a mom. I didn't just want it; I *needed* it to be happy and complete. It was my life's purpose, after all.

As a healthy twenty-four-year-old woman, I figured we'd get pregnant quickly and easily. The first month, when my period arrived, I brushed it off. "No big deal. It'll happen next time." The second month, when my cycle arrived again, I was still optimistic and eager to try again. "Third time's the charm!" But when I didn't get pregnant during month three, four, five, six, seven, eight, and nine...each time, hope dipped a bit lower and my anxiety started to climb.

I dreaded reaching the one-year mark, because most fertility experts urge you to seek medical care if you're unable to conceive within twelve months. The internet just makes it worse. Dr. Google obnoxiously reiterates that time is not on your side when you're TTC even when you're in your twenties.

One year into our journey, I went in for testing. "Everything looks normal," my doctor reported. Menstrual cycles are regular. Hormone levels look good. There's no reason I shouldn't be able to have a baby. The official diagnosis: "unexplained infertility" is exactly what it sounds like. There's no explanation as to why this is happening. My husband got tested too. His sperm count levels were excellent. No issue there either.

While this might seem like good news, it didn't feel like it. My husband hated it. He wanted answers. We both did.

"Why is this happening, and more importantly, *what can we do about it?*"

I wanted a solid action plan: something I could *do* to control what happened next. Whether it was changing my diet, pumping myself up with vitamins, or consulting with doctors or spiritual gurus, I was willing to do whatever it took.

SEARCHING FOR ANSWERS

Shortly after our diagnosis, my mom gifted me a book called *Ask Your Guides* by Sonia Choquette. I couldn't put the book down. Choquette describes an invisible world of guides and angels watching over us, listening to our dreams and desires, and wanting to help—a higher power and plan. As my fertility anxiety spiked, this book gave me hope and assurance of love and support as I navigated this mysterious journey. Reading Choquette's book felt like I remembered where I came from and why I'm here. It answered many of the torturous thoughts of, *Why is this happening to me?*

In one of my frantic "how to get pregnant yesterday" online searches, I stumbled upon a spiritual advisor named Elisabeth Manning. She showed me there's more to this fertility journey than what meets the eye. She taught me how to connect with my spirit and even my baby's spirit. She showed me how to meditate and how to trust what I was seeing in my mind's eye. She was the first person to propose a radical idea: What if the challenges you're experiencing now are preparing you for parenthood? And, what if you're meant to birth more than a child?

Her words resonated with a deeper part of me. Everything I was experiencing—the hopeful trying, the disappointment each month, the shame of not being able to do what my body was supposed to do, the grief when yet another attempt didn't work out—was shaping me into a different version of myself. If I could survive this, I could handle anything. While a part of me felt grateful for the critical life lessons I was learning, all I wanted more than anything in the world was my baby.

FOUR YEARS IN...

By this point, we'd been trying to conceive for about four years. I had tried every single fertility-boosting diet in existence, and every vitamin an apothecary has ever created. I went to acupuncture and naturopaths, hypnotists and Reiki specialists, psychics, and palmists, tarot card readers, and mediums. I was as dedicated to my fertility journey as a monk is to monasticism.

I made avocado mousse for dessert (yuck) and didn't allow myself to have real dairy. I quit coffee (torturous) and sipped warm water with lemon juice, deluding myself that it was "almost the same thing!" (It's so not.) I even considered removing the built-in microwave from our kitchen, fearing the rays would destroy my chances of ever conceiving (because I had signed up for an expensive fertility protocol, and that's what they told me to do).

Fertility is all about expansion and growth, yet my life kept getting smaller. Fewer and fewer foods that I was allowed to eat. Rigid rules that kept me penned in. Even my social life was constricted. I isolated myself from the people that I love, because every time someone asked, "So when are you two going to have kids?" the shame I felt was overwhelming. I was tired of sputtering out awkward replies. So I just stopped going out.

When you work so hard and sacrifice everything that brings you joy, and it doesn't work, it's an absolutely gut-wrenching feeling. Like it's all for nothing. A waste of time that I couldn't afford.

DESPERATE FOR A SOLUTION

Every month, when I could feel my period coming and I would start to see the beginnings of blood on my panties, my heart would drop into my stomach and a lump would land in my throat. The worst part was feeling so responsible when I had to swallow the pain, pretend "everything's fine," and break the news to my sweet and supportive husband. Every month, I felt the agony of breaking his heart all over again too.

As another birthday loomed on the horizon, I was desperate to get pregnant. I tortured myself by dutifully following all the contradictory orders that our culture (and the fertility industry) assigned to me. Because that's what a good mother should do for her child, right? Anything and everything. No sacrifice is too great. Or so I believed.

"SOMETHING'S GOT TO SHIFT..."

After living on the fertility roller coaster for close to five years, I knew, "Something's got to shift." I couldn't carry on this way any longer.

I had always been interested in psychology and recently fell in love with spirituality. So, when I noticed a training program to become a certified Life Coach—led by Martha Beck, a leader in this space and Oprah's personal coach—I signed up on the spot.

I was thrilled for the opportunity to learn from Martha, as I'd spent my entire childhood with my eyes faithfully glued to the television at five o'clock every weeknight for *The Oprah Winfrey Show* while my mom cooked a very '90s pork chop dinner.

Most of my people didn't exactly get it ("What's a life coach, exactly? Is that even a real profession?"), but something pulled me to the program that I couldn't explain.

I quit my cushy, well-paid job at my family's successful auto insurance company and threw myself into the life-coaching training program.

It was time to birth something new in my life.

Martha's program had a beautiful balance of science and spirituality. She's a Harvard graduate who loves ironclad evidence...and a woman who meditates and receives messages from spirit. She was my kind of mentor.

During the certification program, my favorite topic was the *mind–body connection*. I was fascinated with how disconnected we have become from our bodies, how our mental state impacts that physical body, and all the evidence to back this up.

Given everything I'd experienced the last few years, I wondered, *How does my mind impact my fertility, and how can I best support my body?* I threw myself into researching this topic. I was stunned by what I discovered and shocked that none of the doctors or fertility experts had ever mentioned the mind–body connection during one of my zillion appointments.

A NEW PURPOSE

During my life coach certification program, we were invited to consider, "What kind of coach do you want to be after graduating?" Some wanted to become career coaches and help clients land their dream jobs. Others envisioned becoming relationship coaches, assisting couples to find greater intimacy and closeness. Me? I wasn't sure which specialty to choose.

One day, Martha guided us through a meditation. I closed my eyes and surrendered to the process. It was a moment I'll never forget. All around me, in my mind's eye, I could see tiny orbs of light. Thousands. Maybe millions. Twinkling, sparkling, surrounding me. These balls of light felt magnetized to me, and I felt equally pulled to them. There was a profound sense of peace, joy, and childlike wonder. My eyes welled with tears, and I had a deep understanding of *knowing*.

I knew these orbs of light were the spirits of babies waiting to meet their parents.

"This is it," I said with tears streaming down my face and the hairs sticking up all over my body. "This is my life's work: to help these babies and mamas find each other."

THE FERTILITY COACH...WITH NO BABY YET

After graduating, I became an official certified Life Coach and decided to specialize in fertility. I was excited to work with clients, and sometimes I felt like an imposter. How could I help other women get pregnant if I didn't get pregnant yet myself?

I reminded myself, "Trust the science, the tools, and yourself." I had just completed intensive training on the mind–body connection and felt a substantial spiritual pull to this work. Plus, after TTC for what felt like a kajillion years and my nonstop research on the topic, I practically had a PhD on fertility; information galore, plus empathy for my client's situation.

"Also," I reminded myself, "you aren't just showing women how to get pregnant. You're showing them how to have a wildly satisfying life before baby." I remember thinking, "Maybe me not being pregnant yet is exactly what makes me trustworthy and relatable for future clients." This turnaround was huge for me. What I thought was the worst quality about me, ended up being my best.

So, I began working with clients. First, just one or two.

Then three. Then more. Most of these women were just like me. They'd been running on the TTC hamster wheel for years. They were concerned and stressed out. They'd been through month after month of disappointment and grief. And they had tried every fertility-boosting protocol under the sun, growing more discouraged with each failure.

"Okay," I told each new client who arrived at my coaching practice, seeking help. "What you've been doing isn't working. Are you willing to try another way?"

"Instead of fighting the journey and how you feel," I said to my clients, "what if you began to accept it?" Not necessarily the situation. But accept how you're feeling—both the excitement you feel when you imagine yourself with a big growing belly—and the anxiety that bubbles up as you anticipate another doctor's appointment. Accept that there's a part of you that is sad and confused, and then tend to that part of you as you would comfort your future baby. Accept that the timeline isn't totally up to you, and accept that you do have a healthy sense of control over how the journey feels.

"Instead of waiting for a baby to arrive so you can finally start living," I added, *"what if you let yourself fully live your life right now?"*

I encouraged my clients to have date nights, eat pasta (if they were craving it), sleep in, take vacations, and have sex purely for the joy of it (what a concept!), sign up for painting and pottery lessons, and rediscover the simple pleasures of being alive in a human body.

"What if instead of rushing toward your baby, you slow down the pace of your life and allow your baby to come to you?"

I invited my clients to spend time with themselves and to get in touch with their own unique nature. To meditate, journal, drop into their bodies and visualize spending time with their baby. Instead of prescribing a rigid meal plan or supplement regime, I asked my clients to simplify their restrictive wellness plan and do less—less monitoring, less tracking, less controlling, and more ease. And I taught them coaching tools so they could feel safer making these changes.

I educated my clients on the mind–body connection, providing scientific evidence on how your thoughts and beliefs influence your body. I told them, "Let's get your *mind* and body on board, so you can get your baby on board."

Some of my clients were trying to conceive naturally and some were doing IVF. Most of my clients got pregnant within a year.

"Holy shit. This *really* works."

Each time a client shared their happy news, I was thrilled. Even though I wasn't pregnant yet, I was never jealous. My eyes welled with happy tears. My confidence grew, and I knew, "It's only a matter of time before my baby shows up in my life too."

BACK ON THE BABY-MAKING TRAIN

My husband and I eventually decided to pursue IVF. It was a textbook-perfect cycle. Unfortunately, it ended in a miscarriage. Experiencing this loss was a level of grief that indescribably punctured my heart.

I felt waves of vast emotional and physical pain rolling through my body and needed a ton of nurturing and cuddles from my husband during this time—lots of rest, downtime, Netflix, and ordering in chow mein from my favorite Chinese restaurant. I could hear my spirit echoing in my head during this time. "Yes, this hurts, and you're safe to feel the pain inside your body. You get to choose how you respond to yourself." I could choose to think, *I'm a failure and will never be a mom.* Or, I could select a compassionate thought. *I'm grieving. That's okay. I can sit with my pain. And my story isn't over yet.*

After our heartbreaking loss, I spent a few months gathering my strength to do a frozen embryo transfer. By strength, I don't mean it in the stereotypical way of being unphased and bulldozing through. I spent months surrendering deeper into my internal world and allowing myself to feel how I felt without the pressure to be, feel, and act perfectly. I didn't require myself to be "the superwoman" or "the strong survivor" 24/7. At times, I felt empowered and unstoppable. Other times, I wanted to curl into a bed, let out a good cry, and needed tenderness to get through the day. I reminded myself, "I'm a human being. All of these experiences are okay."

Intuitively, I felt my baby was on its way. I spent blissful moments in meditation, connecting with him or her. I slowed my life way down and filled it way up with the people I love, doing the things that I loved—long walks, late nights around the campfire, lattes (hallelujah!), and margaritas on Friday nights. I ate natural, healthy foods most of the time, not just to get pregnant but because I wanted to, and it made me feel alive. I was so in love with my partner. Sex had never been better. I'd still get triggered by specific things like unexpected pregnancy announcements, but I knew how to feed myself compassion and grace to move through it. I had a fulfilling career. Life was better than I could have ever imagined. Having a baby shifted from a desperate need to a happy, healthy desire. I had officially taken the baby off of the pedestal. I knew my worth as a woman, and it was not dependent on my reproductive journey.

When our frozen embryo transfer didn't work, I was dumbstruck. But even then, I knew in my bones that this journey wasn't over yet. It felt like a climactic moment in a movie similar to Joseph Campbell's *The Hero's Journey* when the heroine faces a crossroads: Give up or keep going? This moment felt like a divine test. I wanted to keep going. It didn't mean "try harder, push, and force your way forward." It meant "keep surrendering, trusting, and enjoying your life. It isn't all for nothing."

I asked the Universe to show me a sign that I was on the right path. Just a few hours later, I saw a rainbow after a storm. I took that as confirmation. I wrote a letter to my baby letting him or her know how much I loved them...and how much I loved myself too.

"Dear baby, it's me, your mom. I want you to know I love myself even though I'm not perfect. I hope you'll love me, too, and decide to be part of my life."

Two months after my failed FET (frozen embryo transfer), my best friend asked me if I had gotten my period yet because we were spending so much time together that our cycles synced up.

"No, actually I haven't..."

I'd been so busy living and loving my life that I hadn't been tracking my cycle as closely as I used to. I went home and found an old pregnancy test in my closet. I took the test, and it lit up like a Christmas tree. Eight long years of trying. Ninety-six months of bleeding. IVF. Miscarriage. Failed FET. I tried everything to make it happen and finally learned what it meant to surrender. Letting go of my idealized timeline and need to control. I was leaning into the uncertainty and learning how to love myself (and appreciate all the good in my life) regardless of my ability to reproduce.

I tossed the pee-soaked stick into my husband's lap. Confusion, shock, and delight came across his face and everything moved in slow motion. "This is really happening."

Two years later, I got pregnant once again unexpectedly and easily with a second baby boy.

THE WORST AND BEST THING THAT EVER HAPPENED

Spending eight years trying to conceive was the hardest thing I've ever experienced; the worst thing ever and the best thing too.

Maybe you're saying, "Well it's easy for you to say that now. You have two kids." Nope, I've been saying this since I first became a fertility coach. Pre-baby. My baby was the cherry on top of an already totally awesome life.

I'm so grateful I didn't get pregnant on my first try because I would have missed out on so much growth, which is ironic given how often I thought while TTC that I was falling behind or missing out.

Through my fertility journey, I learned how to tolerate the discomfort of uncertainty (which is an ever-present fact of life before, during, and after pregnancy). I learned how to hold the duality of loving life right now *and* wanting more. How to accept pain and receive pleasure. How to develop trust in both myself, *and* a mysterious yet miraculous force that knows the way. How to embrace my humanity. How to take care of my mental health and my body even during the rockiest times. I have self-soothing abilities now that I didn't have before. I'm a better wife and mom because of the challenges I went through.

I received *so much* on the journey of fertility. And I want the same for you too. It might be helpful for you to imagine Fertility as a living being. A supportive friend or gentle coach. Right now, she's turning to you, saying, "Mama Bear, I have a few messages for you." Are you ready to receive them? Turn the page.

MESSAGES FROM FERTILITY

If Fertility was a living, breathing being, what would she say to you?

What does she want you to know?

What does she want you to let yourself feel?

What does the quality of her presence offer you besides a baby?

What words of wisdom, inspiration, and reassurance can she give you?

What is the truthful and hopeful story she wants you to hear to ease your anxiety?

I want you to feel that each chapter inside this book is a *Message from Fertility*.

Fertility wants to partner with you just as much as you do with her. She has already met your child, and she can't wait for you to hold this being in your arms when they arrive earthside. She knows *your life right now* is a miracle and you are worthy of love, respect, and admiration before you become a parent, and afterward, and in every season of your life.

Fertility is not in a rush. She's not rigid. She doesn't deprive, restrict, or punish. She doesn't force. Yet, she is more powerful than just about anything in our Universe.

She wants to teach you how to create success in all areas of life, not just when it comes to your baby.

She has a few messages for you, Mama Bear.

CHAPTER 1

MIND AND BODY ARE DESIGNED TO WORK TOGETHER

PREPARING YOUR FERTILE GROUND

Your mind is powerful. Your body is powerful too. When you learn how to use both *together*, you become unstoppable in all areas of your life.

Using the mind–body connection might make total sense to you. Or, this might sound too abstract or fantastical. At this moment in the journey, you may want *proof*. You want evidence to feel secure and safe enough to try something new.

Same. When I first learned about how the mind and body work together, I wanted to see Science with a capital S. Many of my clients feel the same way. And that's why, as we begin Chapter 1, we will go through the evidence. In doing so, we're preparing your mind and body for the journey ahead.

In the beginning, when I explored the mind–body connection and applied it to my fertility journey, I felt cautiously hopeful. But I also felt flickers of unease that, yet again, I might end up disappointed. It was tough for me to believe this might work. Like me, you've probably experienced many restless 3:00 a.m. nights rolling around your sheets while arguing and asking, *Why can't you believe your body can do this? Why is it so hard for you?*

To which my loving self would eventually and so gracefully reply, *Spenser, as much as you are an infinite spirit and unlimited in your potential, you have a human fucking brain.*

As much as I hold in high regard the mystery and magic of the Universe, I have a human brain that needs cold, hard facts to trust and actually believe in something new; especially if the past doesn't exactly support my ideal, baby-filled future.

To grow something new—a garden, a baby, a new version of you—the first step is to prepare the soil. Pull the weeds. Pour nutrients. Water the ground. Get it ready, girl. I know how tempting it is to just jump into action, but you can't skip this mental preparation part. And so, I'm going to have a little chat with your prefrontal cortex—the part of your brain that appreciates evidence and research.

LET'S TALK TO YOUR PREFRONTAL CORTEX

This section lies at the very front of your noggin and it is the thinking or reasoning part of your brain. It plays a central role in decision-making, problem-solving, emotional regulation, and the integration of information.[3] It's particularly important for forming and integrating new beliefs that eventually guide your life.

It's the bodyguard part of your brain that says, "Sounds cool and all, but if I'm going to consider a new approach to getting pregnant, then I need evidence that it'll be worth it. Convince me."

It's important to know that this part of the brain goes offline when your nervous system becomes activated by a stressful event. This explains why you may feel so confused and unsure about your next right steps on your fertility journey. It's not that you don't know and can't see. When the prefrontal cortex is offline, it's like wearing foggy, smudgy glasses that impair your vision. In reality, it's just time for a good and thoughtful cleaning. The good news is that this book is designed to engage this area of the brain and shift it into high gear.

Here's the thing: if you're anything like the women I work with, you hold and hear this intuitive whisper that reassures you that you will someday somehow be a mom. It's a gut feeling that keeps you going. But you also have your doubts and stored memories of your trials and tribulations. "Will this work for *me*?" or "But it hasn't happened yet, so why would it happen *now*?"

I know you wish these doubts would vanish. Or maybe you try to pretend they're not there and that everything is "fine." But in my experience, accepting my humanity (my doubts and fears) is much more conducive to change.

Fertility wants you to know: Admitting your fears and your doubts (even any skepticism you have) and exploring how the mind and body work as a collaborative team will only work to complement and reinforce what you intuitively know to be true.

INTUITION AND LOGIC CAN PARTNER TOGETHER

For example, imagine buying a home. Your intuition might give your body a feeling that the house you looked at "feels so right." However, to make sure it's the right decision for you, you need a bit of logic to create internal safety. So you get an inspection on the house, do some research on the neighborhood, and make sure you can afford it. Blending the logic of mind with the intuition of the body instills a sense of security and enthusiasm to trust and take the leap.

One very consistent message I share with women TTC is to meet yourself where you're at. Like me, you too have a *human fucking brain*. Chances are, your brain is currently running old, hardened, neural pathways that are making you feel incapable of conception, and this understandably stresses you the hell out.

Fertility says, "I want you to expand as deeply as possible into creating a supportive and sustainable bond between your mind and body. So, let's dive into the research. Let's pull the weeds. Let's deal with those doubts."

You can do this by bringing it back to the basics.

BABY-MAKING: BACK TO BASICS

As a young woman, you were probably taught that having unprotected sex was super dangerous and you could get pregnant just by looking at a penis. You spent many sexually active years fearing pregnancy and preventing it at all costs. This led you to believe that if it doesn't happen easily and instantaneously, then something must be wrong with you.

In reality, and when explored logically, the recipe for conception is highly complex coupled with a huge dose of mystery and magic.

WHAT WE *KNOW* ABOUT CONCEPTION

Pregnancy occurs when a sperm cell from a male fertilizes an egg cell from a female, resulting in the formation of a zygote, which then implants itself in the woman's uterus and develops into an embryo and later a fetus. The window for this to occur is just a few days of the month if you have a regular cycle. Most likely, you already know this. We all know this! And yet...

WHAT WE *DON'T* KNOW ABOUT CONCEPTION

Fertility is a complex and multifaceted aspect of human biology. While doctors and researchers have made major advancements in understanding it, many aspects remain mysterious or not fully understood, or require more research. There are gaps in our knowledge that even the world's top fertility doctors do not have the answers to.

For example, what is unexplained infertility? Why does treatment work for some couples, but not others? How is it possible to get pregnant naturally after many failed IVF attempts? Why does one woman who's a chain-smoker and eats McDonald's three times a day get pregnant on her first try, whereas another woman who leads a far healthier lifestyle struggles for years? There's no evidence to prove why this occurs. Although, we all (including myself) have our theories.

THE POWER OF THE MIND–BODY CONNECTION

One thing we *do* know (confirmed and verified by copious research) is that what's happening in your mind (what you think, believe, and how you feel) has an impact on your body (your nervous system, digestive system, reproductive system, and all systems in your body).

You secrete more digestive enzymes (or less), speed up your heart rate (or slow it down), dilate your pupils (or contract them), and carry additional oxygen to your reproductive organs (or away from them) based on your mental and emotional states.

Shameful and self-critical thoughts activate your sympathetic nervous system (fight or flight) and cause one type of physiological response in your body. Secure and self-compassionate thoughts engage your parasympathetic nervous system (rest and digest) and create a very different response.

This is not woo-woo. This is science. Proven by mind–body medicine researchers at Harvard. Confirmed by other top institutions too. There's an undeniable connection.

THE DOMAR CENTER OF HARVARD

Dr. Alice Domar was the first researcher to apply mind–body medicine to women struggling with fertility. She is an associate professor in obstetrics, gynecology, and reproductive biology at Harvard Medical School, and a senior staff psychologist at Beth Israel Deaconess Medical Center.

In a 2011 study published in the journal *Fertility and Sterility*, Domar placed TTC women into two groups: women following a mind–body medicine program, and women in a control group who were not.[4]

In the mind–body group, women went through a ten-week program of "relaxation training, cognitive restructuring, and stress management," which led to "significant reductions in anxiety, depression, anger, and fatigue," to quote Silvia Schneider Fox, PsyD, who trained under Domar.[5]

In the mind–body group, 55 percent of the women got pregnant, stayed pregnant, and had a baby. In the control group, only 20 percent did.

And in the mind–body group, out of all the women who conceived, 76 percent got pregnant naturally within twelve months.

Since then, Domar has worked with thousands of women, and her findings have remained consistent. She said, "All the research I have done has shown the same thing: women who participate in a mind–body-based intervention experience pregnancy rates anywhere from two to four times the rate of women who do not participate."[6] She notes that "emotional support, stress management skills, lifestyle advice, and counseling" are important components of a mind–body program for women on their fertility journeys.

The mind–body connection is incredibly powerful, not only for increasing fertility but with every other process in your body too. A few examples...

THE MILKSHAKE STUDY

As reported on NPR, a researcher at Columbia University prepared a large vanilla milkshake.[7] She poured the shake into two containers. One was labeled "Sensishake" and had a nutritional label that said: zero fat, zero sugar, only 140 calories. The other container was labeled "Indulgence" and proclaimed to be full fat, decadent, rich, and 620 calories. In reality, both shakes were exactly the same, and 300 calories per serving.

Then she invited her test subjects to have a glass. Half the test subjects were offered Sensishake. The other half received Indulgence. Nurses measured each person's ghrelin levels before and after drinking their beverage. Ghrelin is "the hunger hormone" and is secreted in your gut when you're hungry to signal to your brain that you need sustenance. If you haven't eaten in a while and feel peckish, or eat a light meal and you're not satiated, your ghrelin levels are higher and tell your brain, "Feed me!"

The people who *thought* they were drinking a low-calorie diet shake had higher ghrelin levels than the people who *thought* they were enjoying a luscious creamy treat. Again, let me repeat: both groups were drinking the exact same beverage! However, the people who believed they were enjoying Indulgence had ghrelin levels that were *three times lower* than the other group. You'd think their bodies would respond exactly the same way, but they did not!

This illustrates the power of your mind. What you believe can trigger your body to secrete more (or less) of a certain hormone. It's true when it comes to your digestive system and your reproductive system too.

THE MAID STUDY

Researchers asked a group of eighty-four housekeepers, "Would you consider yourself to be physically fit?"[8] The majority of the group responded, "No, I rarely get any exercise."

The researchers divided these women into two groups. One half was told, "Actually, you have a very physical job. You're exercising all day long. In fact, you exercise more than most people do! Your lifestyle is very active and healthy." The other half was told nothing (they were the control group).

One month later, all the housekeepers went in for testing. The control group had not changed in any discernible way. However, the group that had been given the "you're active and fit" message transformed. On average, the women in this group lost three pounds, their body composition changed (more muscle and less fat), and their blood pressure improved. Simply by perceiving themselves in a new way—as an active person, fit, strong, and athletic—their physical bodies changed.

THE RATTLESNAKE IN THE ROAD

Byron Katie, the enlightened genius of a method of self-inquiry called "The Work," discusses the mind–body connection by describing a rattlesnake in the road.[9] One day while out walking, Katie saw a rattlesnake just a few feet away. *A poisonous snake!* she thought, recoiling in fear. Her body immediately went into panic mode: heart pounding, vision narrowing, adrenaline surging, all the physiological responses we experience when we're in life-or-death danger. But then Katie noticed, "Oh, actually it's just a stick. Not a snake at all." Immediately she felt calmer.

When you believe there's a threat, your body responds accordingly, even if (in reality) there's no threat and you are, at this moment, completely safe. It's not the external situation that determines the chemical reactions in your body. It's what you think and believe about the situation.

The mind is great at playing tricks on you—convincing you that something terrible is happening when you're okay. Your mind can do the opposite too—keep you feeling safe, secure, and grounded, even when external circumstances are challenging.

Along your fertility journey, your mind can be your friend and ally—gently influencing your body and helping you get pregnant—or your mind can send you into spirals of despair.

Let's say, for example, you're doing IVF. If you believe that IVF is a living nightmare, the last thing you ever want to do, and poisonous for your body, those thoughts will influence your physiology. On the other hand, you can develop a healthy sense of control and label your shots with the words "love" or "calm" and believe (as many of my clients do) that's what you're putting into your body. This way, IVF can be an empowering choice and these thoughts have the potential to influence a different physiological response.

IT'S SO NOT YOUR FAULT

I want to address something head-on. On this fertility journey, there are aspects beyond your control. If you struggle to get pregnant or become pregnant and experience loss, it is not because you "didn't harness the power of the mind–body connection," "didn't do it 'good' enough," or "should have done it more." I want to be clear: I don't believe anything in your thoughts, actions, or feelings makes you responsible for a miscarriage or any kind of loss. Even if you've committed to strengthening your mind and body connection, destiny is at play here. I've faced loss, and it's excruciating. You are not to blame. *It is not your fault.*

Your mind and body connection is not the *only* factor determining a pregnancy, but it's an important one.

We've made it clear that a strengthened mind–body connection can increase your fertility. But beyond that, it can also be used to alleviate suffering along the way—when there's loss, when things don't work out, or when a pregnancy is a bit more complicated than expected. No matter what happens on the journey, mind–body medicine tools can help, and these tools are outrageously overlooked.

A CONNECTION TO A HIGHER POWER AND A HIGHER PLAN

For the TTC community, one aspect of the fertility journey consistently emerges as a source of tremendous solace for them despite their setbacks. And this is a newfound spiritual connection.

From a logical perspective, establishing any kind of mindfulness or spiritual practice, whether that's yoga, meditation, or prayer, is known to lower stress hormones like cortisol and reduce anxiety. These practices have been around for thousands of years for a reason. They *work*.

But science is beginning to catch up to spirituality and its benefits on the mind and body. Emerging research by Dr. Lisa Miller, known for *The Awakened Brain*, explores the relationship between brain well-being and spirituality.[10] In an eighteen-month MRI study involving individuals who hold spirituality or religion in high regard, researchers observed healthier neural structures in the brain compared to those who don't prioritize spirituality. According to Miller, a spiritual foundation is somewhat of a protective buffer against life's challenges.

Not to mention, an unceasing emphasis on the physical body, the statistics, and what's happened so far makes conception feel, well...how do I put this? *Im-freaking-possible.* When the sheer marvel of conception cannot be overlooked—the magical moment when sperm and egg unite, giving rise to conscious physical life—it's a miracle that retains its mystical essence. It's hard to deny there is something bigger at play.

Developing a spiritual practice or belief gives rise to trust in a power and a plan greater than us. And this, to me, is of *great* comfort. The evidence shows both your mind and your body agree. Having a spiritual practice in your life (whatever that looks like for you) can help you handle stress healthier. Which, by the way, is what we need to chat about next.

CHRONIC STRESS VERSUS ACUTE STRESS

I know you've heard this before. Family and friends (with the best of intentions) tell you, "Just relax, and then you'll get pregnant!" Ta-da! Just like that! *Well, thank you for that revolutionary information, Aunt Suzy!* These kinds of comments are insensitive and minimize the genuine pain you're feeling. Plus, it's just not that simple.

Stress isn't something you can just "erase" from your life; further, not all forms of stress are necessarily harmful for you. This topic is more nuanced than that.

What is stress? Stress happens in your mind and body when you resist what is currently unfolding in your life, whether that's a circumstance or a feeling you wish would just go away. Stress occurs when you believe that things shouldn't be the way they are.

What's an alternative to this resistance? How can you gain a healthy sense of control over stress and the fertility journey? Here are a few lessons about stress that I want you to know.

THERE ARE DIFFERENT KINDS OF STRESS. SOME WEIGH MORE HEAVILY ON YOUR BODY. SOME DON'T.

Acute stress is the normal, natural, everyday kind of stress. It's not harmful. Think: you hear a loud noise, and for an instant, your body goes, "WTF was that?" and you feel unsettled for a moment, but quickly recover. Phew. All good. Or you get a passive-aggressive email from a colleague and feel not-so-great about it, but after taking a walk you barely remember it happened, and you're fine. No biggie. It's no longer lingering in your body.

Chronic stress is different. This type of stress is constant, pervasive, and exhausting to your body. It's not a brief momentary thing. It's more like a never-ending dark cloud looming over you. It's what's born out of the thought, *This shouldn't be happening. It's not supposed to go this way.* This type of stress is excessive, outside of the normal range, and can dysregulate your nervous system—the body's communication system that coordinates various physiological functions.

CHRONIC STRESS WEIGHS HEAVILY ON YOUR MIND AND BODY.

Chronic stress can disrupt hormonal balance, menstrual regularity, and ovulation, which can affect fertility. While experiencing chronic stress, blood flow is continually routed away from your reproductive organs and toward your brain for quick thinking to fight off whatever perceived threat is active. Your body is in survival mode rather than "let's make a baby!" mode.

CHRONIC STRESS ISN'T CAUSED BY EXTERNAL CIRCUMSTANCES. IT'S PRIMARILY CAUSED BY HOW WE RESPOND TO THOSE CIRCUMSTANCES.

Here's what I mean by this. Let's say something happens that is completely outside of your control—like your flight is delayed at the airport. What happens next? Do you feel stressed? Or not? Well, this largely depends on how you *respond* to the situation.

If you think, *This is a nightmare, I can't believe this is happening, I always have the worst luck when traveling, my whole trip is fucked*, then your body will perceive, *Danger! We're not okay! We have to tighten up and get ready for battle again!* and release large quantities of cortisol and adrenaline in response to those thoughts.

But if you think, *Okay, well, this sucks and throws a wrench in my plan, but I can rework things,* followed by, *Ugh, I'm annoyed and disappointed, but I can give myself a moment to feel whatever I feel,* and eventually, *All right, I'm still a bit frustrated, but I can make the best of this situation. I'll use this unexpected time to finish reading my book, call a friend to catch up, and go sit down to have a nice meal,* then your body has a very different physiological reaction. Your body perceives, *We're safe*, and your hormone levels reflect this.

I'm well aware that a flight delay does not have the same level of intensity as the struggle to conceive, but it points to the truth that two people can experience the exact same situation—a flight delay—and each person can have a different response to the situation.

Two people. Same circumstance. A completely different set of emotions and, overall, quality of life.

To me, *this is so empowering.* Whether it's big or small, I can't always control external circumstances—a traffic jam on the highway, an aggravating email, a pregnancy announcement from a friend, or not getting pregnant when I want to—but I can choose my response. I can allow myself to feel how I feel, rather than shaming myself for having valid human feelings. And I can choose which kinds of thoughts I will hold in response to whatever's happening around me. In doing so, I'm gaining a healthy sense of control over my stress levels more effectively and creating a more fertile environment in my body. More importantly, I'm so much happier here.

MIND-BODY MANTRA

Things happen all the time that aren't within my control.

However, *I have a healthy sense of control by choosing how I respond to the situation.*

How I respond influences what happens physiologically in my body.

You may be thinking, *This all makes sense, Spenser, but I already know this stuff. I get that chronic stress isn't good for me or my future baby. Knowing this only makes me more stressed out!*

WHEN YOU'RE STRESSED ABOUT STRESS...

I totally get it. When I was TTC, educating myself about how chronic stress can create an imbalance and inflammation in my reproductive system only made me...more stressed!

"I'm too stressed and that's yet another reason why I'm not pregnant!"

I berated myself for not managing my stress levels better. One more thing I wasn't doing "good enough." I beat myself up about it, telling myself, "I should be calmer, I should do more yoga, I should spritz myself with lavender oil, I should move to a forest..." and on and on.

Other times, I felt angry and wanted to scream, "Of course I'm stressed out! I want to be a mom more than anything, and it's not happening, and nobody can explain why! Who *wouldn't* be stressed about that?"

If you're thinking similar thoughts right now, I want to place a gentle hand on your shoulder and validate everything you feel. Your emotions are understandable and human.

The National Institutes of Health published a report on how infertility patients consistently have significantly more symptoms of stress than fertile individuals.[11] So we know there's a definite connection between stress and fertility challenges. But the tricky thing is that it can be difficult to pinpoint which came first—the chicken or the egg? Do you experience high pressure and are you naturally a more anxious person, and that's why your body might be struggling to feel safe? Or because you're struggling to get pregnant, is that why your stress levels are skyrocketing? For many TTC women, it's both at the same time.

Stress can make it harder to conceive, and struggling to conceive can cause added stress. It's a vicious cycle. If you're caught in the middle of this cycle right now, you are not alone.

Two more lessons I want you to understand about stress.

STRESS IS NOT YOUR FAULT.

Life in this day and age is high pressure. Plus, our culture conditions women to be extremely hard on themselves and never feel good enough no matter what we do. You are not to blame for experiencing stress, whether acute or chronic. However, as I mentioned a moment ago, *you can change* your relationship with stress. You can learn tools to handle life differently, and I'll teach you many of those practices in this book.

I believe our bodies are meant and designed to move through stress. It's an ever-present reality of life. It certainly doesn't vanish the moment you become pregnant or the instant your baby arrives. Rather than criticizing ourselves for experiencing stress, and rather than making never-ending and unrealistic self-care to-do lists, we have to consider, "What am I resisting feeling?" "How can I respond to it differently?" To quote the pastor and bestselling author Charles Swindoll, "Life is 10 percent what happens to you and 90 percent how you react."

And lastly,

HAVING SOCIAL SUPPORT ENABLES YOU TO COPE WITH STRESS BETTER.

As reported by the American Psychological Association, a 2022 study found that social support bolsters your resilience in stressful situations.[12] To quote one APA article, "Emotional support is an important protective factor for dealing with life's difficulties." In other words, having high-quality relationships (family, friends, peers who get what you're going through) improves your body's ability to handle stress.[13] Dr. Alice Domar, one of the top researchers on mind–body medicine and fertility, found that having a support group while TTC increases the likelihood of conceiving.[14]

I know how isolating the journey can be. When I was TTC, I didn't feel like I fit in with most women at social gatherings because I didn't yet have a child. I isolated myself and created even more pressure in my mind and body to get pregnant because I believed that only *then* would I fit in. All this created a self-fulfilling prophecy of isolation, when I had such an understandable need and desire to belong.

This is why I *always* encourage TTC women to find a support group, whether in-person, online, or in a coaching program like the one I run, which is called *Fertility Mind–Body Mastery*.

Whatever path you're on, no matter how arduous and challenging it may be, the road is much more manageable when you've got a community of like-minded women to co-regulate with and lean on.

Like my client Ashley D. She was on her TTC journey alone, feeling isolated and exhausted. Joining a supportive group helped her to feel less ashamed and more capable of moving through the emotional highs and lows. Instead of feeling like "the only one," she discovered a whole group of women who have her back.

ASHLEY D.'S STORY

I have wanted to be a mother for as long as I can remember and dedicated my career to working with children and families. I expected to blissfully build a loving family with my husband in the three-bedroom house I had purchased just for that purpose. But my journey took me into unknown and unexpected territory.

I struggled to conceive naturally, did fertility treatments for years, and felt stressed, depressed, and just plain lost. My type-A perfectionist tools of hard work, problem-solving, intellectualizing, and self-suppression were getting me nowhere!

While participating in Spenser's program, I immediately felt relief. Relief that I wasn't alone. Relief that I wasn't doing anything wrong. And especially, relief that I could still feel joy and peace in my life even if I wasn't pregnant yet. I slowly began to believe that I not only deserved to feel those things but those feelings could be the gateway to a fertile life.

Working with Spenser opened my eyes to the fact that I'd been punishing my body in my effort to get pregnant. Following all the "shoulds" and "musts," the fertility rules, and instead of doing what instinctively felt right. And it wasn't just my fertility journey. It was deeper than that. I was living my entire life this way!

I was working in a career that society told me was valuable, even though it left me exhausted and unfulfilled. I was people-pleasing everyone I met to keep up the "good girl" persona that had been reinforced since childhood. I was blaming and shaming myself for doing things that brought me pleasure just because they were seen as "unhealthy" or against mainstream fertility culture. I wasn't even being honest with my husband about what I needed and wanted from him.

Spending time with Spenser and the women in our group felt like an unburdening. Through our discussions, we grew together and supported each other through the highs and lows of the fertility journey and life. I could finally be honest about who I was, and no one shamed or judged me. I could see myself reflected in these women and I wanted their happiness as much as mine.

I have not met my children yet, but I believe more strongly than ever that they are coming. More importantly, I believe I am enough now without them. This process of unlearning, uncovering, and accepting myself has allowed me to be a more true expression of the mother I am meant to be...and the woman I already am.

MIND–BODY EXERCISE: RESPONDING TO STRESS AND TRIGGERS DIFFERENTLY

You do a pregnancy test and it's not the result you want. You have an upsetting conversation with your partner. Someone at work announces she's pregnant. Any of these scenarios might momentarily spike your stress levels.

When you experience heightened stress (a.k.a. intensity in the body), you can't always think or reason your way out of it. Your mind is a powerful tool, but your body wants to be included in the process too. Like Einstein once said, "The mind is a wonderful servant, but an awful master."

Here's a process you can try:

- Begin by breathing into your body and notice how your body feels. Allow for discomfort to arise. What's the physical sensation you're experiencing and where? Silently in your mind, or aloud, name what you feel. "Tight chest." "Hollow heart." "Stomach in knots."
- Breathe again. Speak to the part of your body that feels discomfort. Talk to this uncomfortable sensation as if it's a person you care about. "I see you. I feel you. I'm here with you. I know you are visiting me temporarily and you're here for a reason." Can you let this sensation exist without fearing it will never leave?
- If it's helpful, imagine the uncomfortable sensation in your body is your future toddler throwing a tantrum. What would you do in that situation? Hold them, rock them, stroke their head, let them know that it's okay to feel feelings and that you are right here and not going anywhere. "I know you're upset, and it's okay..." The more grace and patience you offer, the more soothed the child feels, and the faster they can regulate. The same is true for your own body.

When you feel a bit of relief inside your body, your mind returns online. Your prefrontal cortex is functioning again. Now, you can respond to yourself and the circumstance with more awareness and intention. You might say, "Okay, I'm feeling a little out of control now. This is valid. But I'm starting to sense a bit of relief right now. So, I know I can cope with this situation. I know that it's not so much about what happens but more so how I respond to myself in the moment. I'm doing it!"

On the TTC journey, there are moments when you are grieving, tired, or just having trouble remembering things because, um, you're dealing with a lot!

I know it can be hard to digest new information. So I'm wrapping up each chapter with a summary of what we just covered. I hope each summary provides relief and helps these concepts to metabolize more deeply into your mind, body, and even your spirit.

1. Your mind and body are both incredibly powerful. Often, we focus on one or the other, but we're rarely taught how to use them together in a partnership.
2. It's normal to feel skeptical about mind–body medicine. By learning the research behind it, you can help your rational mind to feel more secure in trying a new approach.
3. Research from Harvard shows that TTC women who go through a mind–body medicine program are significantly more likely to get pregnant compared to those who don't.[15]
4. Stress is a normal part of life. You can't erase it. The goal is to learn how to move through it with compassion and care.
5. Using the mind–body connection doesn't mean "thinking positive thoughts." It means understanding how your mind influences your body, having a support network to help you handle the emotional ups and downs on the fertility journey, and having new tools (such as meditation, visualization, journaling, mantras, practices to shift your thinking, and practices to soothe and settle your body) so you can cope with stress differently and get into the optimal state for conception.

CHAPTER 2

THERE IS ANOTHER WAY

YOU HAVE OPTIONS

My mom and I attended a retreat in Phoenix, Arizona, with my Life Coach teacher Martha Beck and the bestselling author of *Eat, Pray, Love* Elizabeth Gilbert. The retreat with this dynamic duo was called *Magic*.

To be honest, we had no idea what we would learn. But something pulled us toward it, and we knew that, duh, it would be magic. Take my money!

As the retreat began, we settled into our seats, and there was a hum of electricity and anticipation in the air. Attendees were there from around the world, and some had traveled thousands of miles to hear from these two women whom we all respected. Everyone was chatting quietly, excited for the experience to begin. Martha and Liz arrived and walked to the front of the room.

"You wanna know how to follow the path out of our culture and back into your nature?" Liz Gilbert asked the audience.

The whole room went so quiet you could hear stomachs growl.

"It's not stressful," she whispered.

Most people need to yell to make their point clear. Liz whispered the truth so gently, and for this reason, it felt all the more powerful.

Like most women, I'd been told (countless times) to relax, calm down, chill out, and stop stressing. But those messages were usually a response from someone uncomfortable with my big, vulnerable, and sometimes anxious presence, and not because they genuinely wanted me to have a better life. They were telling me to relax because my big emotions made them feel uncomfortable.

But it hit me differently when Liz expressed that the path to joy and success doesn't have to be stressful. Liz's message landed in every cell of my being.

It made me realize that the tightness we often feel in our bodies could be an affirming message from nature whispering, "Come back. It's wonderful here. It doesn't have to be this hard. I got you."

Mama Bear, up until now, the path to conceiving a child has felt draining. Society has conditioned you to believe that getting what you want is hard work, and if you're not succeeding, it's because you're lazy, not working hard enough to get it, and maybe not cut out to do this whole parenting thing.

Your path to pregnancy has felt so overwhelming because you didn't know you had any other options. There's the conventional path that's laid out for you. We all have a primal drive to follow the pack—an instinctive old fear that we will die of loneliness and starvation if we don't follow what everyone else is doing.

Fertility wants you to know: You have options.

And the path forward isn't meant to be stressful.

There are thousands of different paths that lead to your child. You might conceive naturally or with the support of modern medicine. You might conceive on your first try, fiftieth try, or hundredth try (like me). No matter how the journey unfolds, it doesn't have to be so triggering, grueling, and miserable. Even if your journey happens to include needle pricks, highly anticipated phone call updates, surgeries, and a great deal of waiting, the journey can still be empowering.

How can you be present on the journey, even when it's so hard?

You do this by following *your* nature. *Your* needs. *Your* version of what feels true, right, and suitable for *you*.

No matter what happens today, tomorrow, or next week on your fertility journey, remember you always have options. The option to part ways with your current doctor and hire someone new. The option to take a break from trying to conceive if you need time to process what you've experienced, grieve, heal, and recharge. The option to keep walking forward but with a new perspective (or a new support group of women surrounding you).

Fertility is endlessly creative and always generates the next right move for *you*.

You are never out of options.

This is true, even if you've already tried so much and don't yet have your baby.

A telling case is my client, Kaitlin, who underwent all the testing, experimented with all the diets, and sought advice from all the experts to try to heal her cycle and conceive. She believed personal sacrifice was a prerequisite for deserving a child. Programmed to conform and obey the fertility industry's restrictive standards, she pushed through despite feeling drained and ashamed for her apparent shortcomings. Until she realized that when you know what doesn't work, you are just getting closer to what does.

KAITLIN'S STORY

I was more than a year into my all-consuming hormone journey, trying to get my period back by any means necessary. That's when we learned that my husband and I are both carriers of a rare and life-threatening genetic disease. What are the fucking chances? Our fertility clinic told us, "Because of this risk factor, the safest route to conceive would be IVF."

I didn't want to do IVF. Fear and grief hit me hard. I felt blindsided and my mind spun with all the worst-case scenarios. Physical, emotional, and financial suffering, just like I'd seen in movies when characters struggle with fertility. I felt an enormous loss of self. I was a strong, healthy, athletic girl my whole life. What happened to get me here? What went wrong? What did I do wrong? How did I mess up my hormones and health this much?!

I spent the rest of the year manically hunting for a solution. From naturopaths, acupuncturists, dietitians, functional nutritionists, health coaches, therapists, and even energy healers and hypnotherapists at my most desperate point. None of these experts restored my monthly cycle. And the constant lab work was exhausting and made me feel worse about the state of my health.

Each specialist had a different theory about what was supposedly wrong with my body. "It's your hormone levels." "Your immune system is weak." "Your gut health is out of whack." "You have toxicity from cleaning products." I was constantly being told, "You have a problem," and you need to cleanse, detox, and do better. It was like playing wellness whack-a-mole—impossible to prioritize all of these different areas. I kept trying, failing, and blaming myself for not trying harder.

I reached a breaking point and knew I couldn't live like this. I wanted a family, but I didn't want to skid into motherhood, feeling like a hollow shell of myself. That's not the kind of mother and woman I wanted to be. I was on a never-ending cycle of lab tests, fearmongering, and never feeling I was enough. And I wanted off.

That's what led me to Spenser and her Fertility Mind–Body Mastery program. This was the first place on my fertility journey where I was told, "You are already okay." This program gave me permission to stop trying to fix my body at the expense of my happiness. It took me several weeks to wrap my head around the idea that I didn't have to follow such restrictive rules. The strict fertility diet, the gut-healing protocol, all the rules that had dominated my life. With baby steps and patience, I slowly learned to let this go. I realized how much better I felt mentally and physically. Spenser taught me how to trust myself.

As I write this, I am four months postpartum with a healthy and happy-as-hell baby girl conceived via IVF, on our first embryo transfer. But the true miracle is that I've gained even more than a daughter. I regained my joy of living in the simple daily moments. I regained my freedom to vacation with my husband, eat at beautiful restaurants, and celebrate our anniversary with our favorite bottle of champagne. I regained my confidence in my body and my own ability to make decisions for its well-being. All before getting pregnant.

Most importantly, I am restoring my relationship with myself. My daughter will not grow up with a frazzled, stressed-out mom who constantly looks to "the experts" for a rule book on what to do. She'll grow up with a different role model. A woman who is calm, steady, and who knows, "I have enough information to make my own decisions," and "I am already enough."

If Fertility was a living being—a wise mentor or even a cool best friend—she would nudge you to release the rigid fertility rules that have governed the vast majority of your journey until this point.

She would say, "Don't add more to your to-do list. Subtract. Cut your to-do list in half."

She would remind you, "You are allowed to feel how you feel. It's okay to not feel okay. But (and this part might feel strange at first) it's also okay to feel good."

"Yes, you want a baby," she affirms. "But this journey doesn't have to be a full-time job. It doesn't have to take over your entire life. It doesn't have to be so debilitatingly exhausting."

RESISTANCE IS NORMAL

Perhaps there is new hope and excitement bubbling up inside your mind and body. If so, *yes!* But I wouldn't be surprised if you were, too, feeling a bit of resistance.

No, no, no, you think, *I need to do more, not less. I need to work harder. If I do less that means I am being lazy, apathetic, or delusional. Doing less sounds like giving up.*

When considering a new and gentler approach to fertility, resistance is so normal.

It can feel odd and counterintuitive to question our culture's strict fertility rules. Society conditions us to be good girls and rule followers, especially when the command comes from someone in a position of authority. We follow dutifully, without questioning anything, even when the rules conflict with one another.

Should you eat full-fat dairy or does dairy cause inflammation? Have sex every day or every second day? Is yoga the optimal workout for TTC, or should you go for a run to get that heart rate elevated? So many fertility rules are contradictory, causing us to feel like no matter what we do, we're fucking up and can't ever get it right.

As much as fertility experts have good intentions, these rules always made me feel like, "I can't trust myself. I can't trust my body. Worst of all, I can't trust feelings of peace, joy, and pleasure. Because if I feel good, I must not be working hard enough."

Obediently listening to the experts' orders (without questioning any of them) only took me further away from myself, and further away from my built-in baby compass.

For a long time on my TTC journey, I felt like my worthiness as a woman was based on how many rules I could follow impeccably and how many enjoyable things I could sacrifice. How much stress I could endure. How many appointments I could pack into my day. How little joy I could live off of.

The societal pressure to follow the rules is a feeling of physical force. I did this for years, and I did it as hard and as fast as I could. Until I realized, just like my client Kaitlin, that once I knew what didn't work, I was getting closer and clearer on what would work.

I had spent so many years looking outside of myself for answers when my lifeline to the relief I was yearning for was inside of me all along.

When I allowed myself to feel at ease with the present moment, when I stopped rushing from one fertility-enhancing meal plan to another, and when I gained a sense of self that felt whole and complete—*even though I wasn't pregnant yet and even though I wasn't doing everything perfectly*—I felt something new in my body. It was a tiny little flicker of *peace*. For just the briefest moment, I felt *okay*.

"I'm okay right now. I'm okay with my life as it is. I'm okay even though I'm not pregnant yet."

But as soon as this feeling of ease arrived, my nervous system tried really hard to push it away. Resistance came crashing in. There was an energy inside of me reacting with alarm bells that screamed, *"Danger! Nope! Not okay!"*

You might experience the same thing: a brief moment of peace followed by overwhelming resistance. Because of how we're raised by our parents, school system, corporate cultures, religion, and other big influencers, it can feel irresponsible, naive, and even cocky to try a different approach to fertility—one that feels like surrender rather than constant striving.

Women often feel like, "If I do less, then I won't get anything done." You'll spend every day binging mind-numbing reality TV while Dorito-munching your way through your lazy life, slowly spending the rest of your useless existence falling deeper into the crack of your old, dirty couch. The example is dramatic but I'm not far off, am I?

Here's something you may not know, Mama Bear. Research shows that compassion is more motivating than shame. People who speak kindly to themselves experience higher levels of motivation and are more likely to make positive changes in life. Shame keeps you frozen in place. Compassion moves you forward.

And yet, actually being nice to yourself can feel extremely strange at first. For me, it took some time to build trust that I could do less, surrender more, be enough (without necessarily being perfect), speak to myself like a friend instead of a tyrant, and still be safe in my own life.

Fertility wants you to know: Your body might be unfamiliar with experiencing kindness, with receiving compassion, with feeling okay. These sensations might feel alien and uncomfortable. You may feel resistance at first. But this doesn't mean you're doing anything wrong. It's a sign you're shifting in a new and beautiful direction.

Knowing this is a normal part of the process, let's learn a bit more about why we unconsciously resist favorable change.

YOUR UPPER LIMIT

Dr. Gay Hendricks, author of *The Big Leap*, coined the term "Upper Limit Problem." He says we all have a built-in success thermostat. When we start to push beyond our normal and accustomed level of success (love, abundance, safety), we subconsciously engage in beliefs and behaviors that bring us back down to our normal comfort zone. Not because we hate ourselves, but to protect ourselves.

You may have seen this Upper Limit Problem play out in your career. For instance, you get an exciting promotion, a dream client, or an opportunity that's bigger than anything you've gotten in the past. You're thrilled! But then, you subconsciously sabotage yourself without intending to.

You put the wrong date in your calendar and miss an important meeting, or you make a costly error on the project. Without wanting to, or meaning to, you sabotage yourself because this level of success is too unfamiliar, and therefore, too uncomfortable, and so your brain knocks you back down a peg or two. Down to that comfortable zone on the thermostat.

You will likely hit an upper limit on your fertility journey when you allow yourself to do less. When you embrace the possibility that maybe, just maybe, you are worthy of love without needing to be robotically perfect. When you make a choice about your body based on your instincts rather than following someone else's guidelines. When you momentarily feel okay. As you hit your upper limit, your brain might react with fear, alarm bells going off. "We're hitting an upper limit! This is unfamiliar terrain! Too good to be true!" You feel resistance and begin to second-guess yourself.

The Upper Limit Problem is common with the women whom I work with. Sometimes I'll spend the first couple of months coaching the same person over and over again on the same sticky topic: that it's okay to feel okay on your fertility journey, not just when you reach the baby destination. And that feeling okay actually increases your chances of conception.

My clients want to believe this is true. Yet they feel tremendous subconscious pushback. Because your body has collected memories and experiences through both your current life and your ancestral lineage lines, and all of these collective experiences have taught you, "If there's something you want, you'd better work harder than anybody else to get it. The harder you work, the more deserving you will be. You need to be ready to fight." This is what you've been trained to believe and anything else feels profoundly uncomfortable at first.

This journey doesn't have to be a fight, with your fists balled up and your stomach clenched tight. It can feel different.

Fertility wants you to know: You're safe to feel okay right now.

If feeling okay feels very strange—like a new color you haven't seen before in your entire life—resistance will come up, and resistance is okay too.

When you hit your upper limit and have that feeling of, "This is too good to be true," imagine Fertility whispering to you, "It is good *and* it is true." Close your eyes and visualize yourself turning a thermostat up higher. Previously, you could only tolerate 15 degrees Celsius of peace and pleasure. But now, you can experience 16. Next month, perhaps 17, as you continue to expand your capacity for joy. As your upper limit keeps rising. All in baby steps.

Fertility wants to wrap you close in a hug and offer the reminder that, deep down, some wise and ancient part of you already knows: You can have what you desire without fighting so hard to get it. And you can feel okay on the way toward it.

NOW IS THE TIME

Many women tell themselves, "When I have my baby, *that's* when I'll finally feel okay."

We postpone being adventurous, or feeling content and worthy until a future date or future circumstance.

Holding our breath for those two pink lines to show up.

"Once I have my baby..."

"I'll accept my doubts, my humanity, my sensitive heart, and my big emotions."

"I'll be more compassionate to myself."

"I'll quit my shitty job."

"I'll show up to the baby shower."

"I'll figure out how to handle the uncertainty of life."

"I'll voice my honest opinions to my in-laws."

"I'll enjoy my favorite foods and hobbies, enjoy my marriage, and enjoy my life."

"I'll stop punishing myself with all the rigid wellness plans and learn to trust my body's cues."

"I'll feel like I've done enough, I have enough, and I am enough."

That's what we tell ourselves. It's just another version of, "Once I lose ten pounds, then I'll deserve to have a wonderful partner...," or "Once I have $100,000 in my savings account, then I'll be able to exhale, relax on weekends instead of working, and have more fun..."

In a hundred different ways, we tell ourselves, "I don't deserve to enjoy my life right now. I don't deserve to be loved, and I don't deserve all the good stuff right now. One day in the future I *might* deserve these experiences. But not yet."

And so, we lie to ourselves and say, "Once [XYZ] happens, then I'll generously allow myself to experience all the things I've been denying myself."

But it never works like that.

Even when you lose ten pounds, you still don't feel worthy of a loving relationship and you decide that, actually, you need to lose another five pounds first, deal with that cellulite, smooth out those wrinkles, and then maybe you'll be worthy.

Even when you make that big pile of money, you still don't feel secure and you'll hustle hard to come up with another benchmark you need to reach first.

And even when the baby comes, your brain and body will still be wired to withhold. You'll come up with some new excuse as to why you can't feel okay about your life. You'll spend your life dangling a carrot of comfort and care and never feeling safe enough to receive it.

Having a child does not make it easier for you to choose you. If anything, it becomes way harder. That's why it's best to learn this lesson before you become a parent. Now, not later.

Fertility wants you to consider:

MIND-BODY MANTRA

What kind of mama do I want to be? Can I be her now?

Do you want to be the mama who continually postpones joy until some date in the distant future? Or the woman who allows herself to experience happiness and her full self now? What's the example that you want your child to watch and follow?

Fertility wants you to know: You can have exciting goals that you're moving toward *and* you can enjoy the journey toward them right now. Both of these can exist simultaneously. You are worthy of the best that life can offer—enriching relationships, energizing hobbies, luxurious vacations, free time in your day, yummy meals, beautiful clothes that fit your current size whatever it may be—and you're worthy of these things yesterday, today, tomorrow, and always. Your best life doesn't start on the day you get pregnant or the day your baby arrives. It's already here. You may tell yourself, "Once I have my baby, then everything in my life will feel just right and I'll finally be the woman I have always wanted to be, and have a life that really means something."

What if that woman is already here?

What if that life already surrounds you?

Fertility wants to gently, softly remind you: You can enjoy the journey, not just the destination. You can feel okay even though aspects of your life are messy but a gorgeous work in progress. The birth of your child is not the moment when your life becomes meaningful and miraculous. Your life is already a miracle. The miracle doesn't begin nine months in the future. It's already here. Honey, it's *you*.

To help root you more fiercely into the *journey* toward your baby, it can really shake things up to ask yourself the same path-altering question my client Steph asked herself when making the shift from sacrifice to simply savoring the moments of her life.

STEPH'S STORY

I was never that little girl who played with dolls, pretending to be the mom. But for as long as I can remember, I knew I wanted to have children.

In my thirties, I felt my biological clock ticking and inquired about freezing my eggs. I was told I wasn't a good candidate because my egg count was too low. A few years after that, I found the person I wanted to start a family with. I told him within weeks of meeting that we might have a longer journey toward pregnancy if that's where things eventually led. When we did start trying, I didn't fully comprehend how lengthy and difficult it would be.

Like many of Spenser's clients, I spent years trying to control my fertility journey. I stripped joy and pleasure from my life, thinking this would help me get pregnant faster. It didn't.

After connecting with Spenser and the women in her program, I noticed a change in life. It was slow until it wasn't. I stopped feeling like a victim. I stopped making my fertility journey all about suffering. I went on strenuous hikes, had drinks without guilt, and simply enjoyed my life.

I considered, "How do I want my future child to live?" I want them to feel joyful and adventurous, not rigid, impatient, or controlling. I want my child to love themself unconditionally, rather than only liking themself when they're doing things "perfectly." So, I need to lead by example. It starts now and it starts with me.

I'm not pregnant yet. But I know my desire to be a mother will come to fruition in divine timing. Until that time comes, I will continue to enjoy the journey of my precious life.

THE ENERGY OF RECEIVING

Expanding your feeling of okayness, goodness, and liveliness requires expanding your capacity to receive.

Biologically speaking, when a sperm is released, it swims up the vagina, through the uterus, and into the fallopian tubes to find the egg. The sperm wiggles and hustles its way into being the first one accepted to fertilize. It's a prime example of a very masculine energy of doing and giving.

When the egg is released, your ovary pops her out, and then... *she just chills*. With her queen energy, she sits and waits to be fertilized. This is an ideal example of the feminine energy of being and receiving.

I remember hearing (obnoxiously often) that the energy of femininity and fertility is a *receptive* energy. Not passive or apathetic, but *receptive*. There's a subtle difference.

It sounds great in theory, but many women (myself included) are so accustomed to doing the exact opposite. We know how to push, grind, and achieve our goals no matter the cost. We know how to drink coffee nonstop, push past the tiredness, and get shit done. We know how to throw our hair into a topknot, roll up our sleeves, answer "just one more email," and do another load of laundry instead of taking the night off. We know how to give generously to the people in our lives: family, friends, colleagues, and clients, even when we're worn out and giving from an empty cup. What we don't know is how to *receive*.

From a mind–body perspective, imagine what happens to a body when the mind is trained to give, give, give, and doesn't know how to receive. The body becomes completely exhausted and depleted of the energy needed to do things like make a baby.

Just like the little sperm dudes, we understand the masculine approach to making things happen. It's how most of us have been taught to get through our lives.

You may be a high-achieving woman who has accomplished so much—impressive degrees, a successful career, an excellent reputation among your peers, and a certain level of financial security. And you may be confused as to why the same work ethic that brought you success in the past isn't working when it comes to getting pregnant.

Why isn't it working? Because fertility is *different*. Fertility is about receiving. It requires a feminine approach to creation, which (for many women) is new and super awkward at first.

The spirit of your baby wants to be raised by a mother who believes, "My worth is not determined by my output." "I can do less and have more."

Your baby wants you to learn how to work smarter, not harder.

Your baby doesn't want you to suffer and sacrifice to get what you want.

Your baby wants you to know that the more you receive, *the more you can give*. Don't you want the same for yourself and your family?

My client Mary was a stepmom to two boys. She was in the midst of IVF and was feeling her stress levels climb when the boys—whom she loved dearly—had a classic teenager moment. Think snotty comments, eye rolls, teen angst, the whole nine yards.

"I just want to lock myself in my room!" she said on our coaching call.

"So why don't you?" I responded.

I could see that Mary needed to receive space, alone time, and nervous system regulation while her husband cared for the boys. This is a great example of how receiving doesn't always mean receiving a gift from someone else. It can also mean noticing your own very understandable basic human needs and giving *yourself* what you need. In Mary's case, this meant a few moments of silent, teen-free time to decompress during this vulnerable time of an IVF cycle. She allowed herself to receive what she needed—and soon, felt much better. (Also, got pregnant with a baby girl on that cycle to balance all the testosterone in their household!)

So, Mama Bear, how can you slowly begin to shift into the energy of receiving? What does this look like? Feel like? Is it receiving and accepting the basic needs of your humanity and locking yourself in your room when you need that space? Is it more like receiving something that you love doing, like watercolor painting or lunch dates with your girlfriends? Or is it time to offload some tasks that take a lot out of you, like hiring someone to clean your home or scheduling a monthly mani–pedi appointment? Like anything else, it's a new skill to learn.

You can practice receiving in small ways, at first.

Allow yourself to receive a compliment without fighting it. Say thank you rather than, "Oh no, c'mon, that's not true."

Allow yourself to receive a gift of any kind. Say, "How wonderful! I love it!" instead of, "No, no, it's too much, really, you didn't have to..."

At the end of yoga practice, instead of skipping Savasana and hurrying on with the rest of your day, stay and linger for ten minutes.

At a coffee shop, order the decadent cinnamon-sprinkled fancy latte that you really want, and savor every sip, instead of ordering the item you feel you "should" get.

Ask for something that seems like it's "too much" ("Honey, can you make dinner tonight so I can lay down and rest?") and then allow yourself to sit down and fully receive (and feel) exactly what you asked for, even if it feels very odd to just...sit there.

These little moments when you feel prickly and uncomfortable when you ask for more than you normally would, when you allow yourself to receive more than you have in the past, *this is your work*. In these everyday moments at the coffee shop, at the kitchen table, or on the couch, you're learning how to tune into the vibration and gift of receiving.

Because of my perfectionist tendencies, I believed that if a new skill didn't come easily to me, then I was failing. If it wasn't a breeze on my first try, I must not be doing it right. For example, after asking my husband to cook dinner after a long day, it felt so strange to relax on the couch and actually let him do it. It didn't feel natural at all. I was practically chewing my nails off with guilt. Or when I decided to take a 2:00 p.m. nap to combat the adrenal fatigue I faced from years of striving, I spent the whole time in bed shivering with shame, as I compared myself to the millions of people working at their desks in the middle of the day. Or when I decided to say yes to a gluten-sugar-dairy-filled birthday cake at my dad's birthday party, I thought I was weak and felt like, "I must not want a child bad enough."

If we're not able to receive the goodness and simplicity of our partners nurturing us with delicious food, or a nap when exhaustion from the world's demands sets in, or a small treat to celebrate the life of someone you love, then how in the world can you expect to receive something as big as your baby?

Fertility wants you to know: It's time to give less and receive more.

Receiving more is uncomfortable at first. But you can handle being uncomfortable. Because discomfort is simply a sensation in the body. Sensations are temporary.

As you begin to receive more, you may subconsciously engage in self-sabotaging behaviors, not because you want to screw yourself over, but to protect yourself and stay in your accustomed-to-comfort zone. Notice when these sabotaging tendencies arise. Notice the resistance, and notice the urge to backpedal into your old patterns. Speak to yourself gently. Say, "I know it's odd and uncomfortable to receive. I know it's much easier to do, do, do, because that's what I'm used to. I get it. But learning how to receive is a good part of my life. I can do this. Feeling awkward is part of the process."

For me, expanding my capacity to receive literally felt like a detox. I noticed physical discomfort and withdrawal symptoms—shaking, trembling, and feeling like something was wrong, like turbulence on a plane. It felt worse before it felt better.

Plus, we've been influenced to expect "the other shoe to drop" by hidden forces. For example, my husband and I were watching a movie the other day, cozying up on the couch together. And there was this scene where everyone was so happy, so smiley, and things were going so good. *Too* good according to Hollywood. My husband screamed, "Something bad's about to happen!" and he was right. We've literally been brainwashed by the media to expect shit to hit the fan when things are feeling good, and it's just not true. These movies, in my perspective, mirror society's discomfort in embracing greater love and goodness that we possess the capacity to hold—for ourselves, others, and the promise of our future.

As you break the generational pattern of over-giving, exhaustion as a status symbol, and always doing more, things will unquestionably begin to feel lighter and easier.

Picture a very small balloon the size of a walnut. Right now, your capacity to receive might be so small just like this miniature balloon. As you practice receiving—gifts, nourishment, free time, kindness, care, and good things from yourself and from others—your capacity expands. The balloon fills with air, more and more, and it grows bigger. A nut, then a plum, then a pumpkin. With each passing day, your capacity grows as you shift into the energy of receiving. And one day, receiving doesn't feel so uncomfortable anymore.

As you expand your capacity to receive, you bring your baby closer to you. Just like the egg with her queen energy, you stay put. You trust. You allow. You receive and attract all the best things in life.

Along the way, you realize you were born to receive so many miracles. A beautiful baby...and many more miracles too. The miracle of a life that you deeply enjoy. The miracle of close, nurturing relationships where people take care of *you*. The miracle of liking and even loving yourself. All of these treasures and more. Mama Bear, they're yours to receive.

You can do this, even (or especially) if right now, your life is crazy with a demanding family or career that asks a lot of you.

Take it from my client Cindy, a dedicated OB-GYN physician who saw pregnant patients daily while struggling with her own fertility struggles. Despite her purely academic intellect, Cindy knew she couldn't deny the power of the mind–body connection. After enough giving and enough suffering, she decided it was *her* time to receive. To receive permission to feel how she felt and a new relationship with herself. And eventually...to receive her beautiful baby boy.

CINDY'S STORY

I had done everything right. I had followed all the rules since I was a kid. I was a board-certified OB-GYN physician with a wonderful husband and a perfect home. But there was a suffocating frustration and an aching absence I felt each day before I had the opportunity to learn from Spenser.

I was angry, resentful, bitter, and exhausted. I was drowning in my career. I was relentlessly bombarded and triggered by my family members, by my friends' pregnancy announcements, and also by my patients. It didn't make sense to me how so many of my patients could get pregnant so easily when they were so unhealthy or on contraception, some for the third time in the four years I tried to conceive.

I had undergone my first FET and miscarried at about eight weeks. I chose medical management to complete my miscarriage. While I was in the most excruciating pain, I remember having this wave of emotion come over me. I told myself to get up because this is not over. A voice in my head said, "This is a new beginning and you will be a mother someday."

A few days later, I found Spenser. I remember having a flood of feelings when I spoke to her. I was a barreling train of emotion heading nowhere and then she asked me, "How does that feel in your body?" With that question, it was like I was frozen, a deer in headlights because I couldn't answer. I struggled to find my words. It was a completely different way of being and it was an eye-opening, cathartic breath of fresh air. I was ready for the change.

I decided to work with Spenser when I knew I had only good things to gain from this learning experience. It was so different from what

I was used to in all my formal education and yet it made total sense. When we get nervous, some of us get gut issues or nausea. When we panic, our palms start to sweat or our mouth gets dry. I was aware of this mind–body connection, but I did not know how to navigate it and steer its energy purposefully into creating my baby. It was an amazing lesson for me and it was complementary to all that I had learned in my education as an OB-GYN physician.

To work with Spenser is to find the eye of your storm. I learned how to find flow and tap into the energy of creation. To be kind and less judgmental of myself and of others. To be open to possibilities versus discouraged by fear. All of this is life-changing for the journey of parenthood as well, as I did eventually conceive, in my forties, shortly after working with her. On my fertility journey, I've learned how to be a better mother, wife, sister, friend, and physician.

MIND-BODY EXERCISE: CLUES TO
KNOW YOUR UNIQUE NATURE

Spend some time exploring these questions in your journal or discuss them aloud with someone you love.

What did you love to do as a child?

What's your favorite smell?

What's your favorite taste?

What's your favorite sound?

When do you lose track of time?

What's your favorite environment?

What is your favorite little thing to receive?

What activity do you find most relaxing?

Can you let yourself have these aspects of your life, and with more presence?

Can you remember a time in your life when something wonderful happened unexpectedly, miraculously, or surprisingly...with ease rather than force? (Like meeting your partner? Connecting with a wonderful friend? Or even something much smaller, like getting upgraded on a flight when you didn't expect it?)

1. Creating a baby doesn't have to feel like grinding, striving, forcing, punishment, or deprivation—which is how your journey may have felt in the past. There is another way to approach your fertility journey. It gets to be this good.

2. If it feels backward or counterintuitive to let yourself feel okay, that's understandable. You've been raised in a society that tells you, "You have to work harder to get what you want," and if you don't succeed, it's because you didn't try hard enough.

3. Notice when you hit your "Upper Limit" and subconsciously self-sabotage your joy, in order to stay in your familiar comfort zone. Be willing to feel the discomfort that naturally occurs when you increase your normal level of happiness.

4. You can practice connecting with the energy of receiving *today*—notice when and allow good things to come to you. Let compliments, help, or love fall into your lap (or womb), rather than making it happen all by yourself.

5. Fertility also wants you to know, "Don't postpone joy until later, when you have a baby." Learn to feel whole, complete, and excited about your life right now. The more you allow yourself to enjoy your life as it is, the more at peace you become, and the more you bring your body into the best possible state for conception.

CHAPTER 3

FEEL THE FULL SPECTRUM OF EMOTION

While I was TTC, I spent many mornings in my bathroom getting ready for the day, brushing mascara onto my lashes while listening to one of those Law of Attraction podcasts or audiobooks. I can't remember which one it was (there were many), but I remember hearing instructions to the tune of:

"If you truly believe, then it will happen."

"Be in the undeniable vibration of positivity, and it will come to you."

"Leave your fear at bay, and your dream is inevitable."

Well, shit! I thought. *That's all?*

I would jump into my car, turn the music up in celebration of my new it's-inevitable-that-baby-is-coming plan, and happily head to work.

I vowed to myself, *Just think POSITIVE THOUGHTS and you'll get everything you want. Including that baby!*

But then, *life* would happen. There was traffic. Someone said something that hurt my feelings. Plans were unexpectedly canceled. I got my period. Or worse, my sister-in-law announced she was pregnant...*again*. My positivity plan would fly out the window. As much as I wanted to "think positive," I just couldn't stay in that place 100 percent of the time. And whenever I felt anything besides pure positive vibes—frustration, disappointment, annoyance, and other very normal human emotions—I got so mad at myself for not being positive enough.

When I was sad, I tried to stuff it down and not let it in. When I was happy, I tried to claw tightly to the feeling so it would never leave. It didn't matter how I was feeling, I was on guard and gripping, trying to control my emotions with perfect, robotic precision.

I spent years trying to zen out, be unfazed, super chill, a.k.a. perfect. Spoiler alert: I never attained perfection. But what I did attain was a great deal of unnecessary suffering. I constantly felt angry at myself for falling short of my impossibly high and unnatural standards.

THE PROBLEM WITH PERFECTIONISM

The problem with perfectionism is that it's 100 percent not possible. But it has a way of convincing you, through its series of sneaky lies, that if you just do everything "right," then it will take you to your baby. Even though perfectionism's version of "right" is absolutely impossible to attain, the crumb trail it leaves behind brings you right back to where you started from.

Brené Brown said, "When perfectionism is driving, shame is riding shotgun."

Shame's primary message is, "Something must be wrong with me."

When you're TTC and it's not happening, it can seem like

there's a great deal of evidence proving that something is indeed wrong with you. You're lazy, unhealthy, weak, not disciplined enough, too uptight, and obviously missing something. So you listen to shame's message and in response, you try to perfect every single freaking thing that you do.

Generally speaking, when you're TTC, perfectionism instructs you to follow a highly subjective healthy diet, take vitamins every day (sometimes multiple times a day), have lots of sex but only at certain times, stay on top of every single bodily symptom, do all the tests, hire all the experts, and saturate your mind with only high vibrational, positive emotions.

"Do all of this. Do it perfectly. And boom, you'll get pregnant," perfectionism whispers to you.

The absolutely crazy thing is that, at the moment when you're jotting down this perfect plan, it actually sounds doable. But then, inevitably, you can't follow through with it. Why? Because, and I can't emphasize this enough, you are a living, breathing human being who is experiencing what it's like to be alive—a life with seasons, fluctuations, and challenges. A body that periodically needs extra care. A mind that needs to be unashamed for the pieces of life—including your emotions— that you can't totally control.

For example, and these are occurrences for every human on the planet, you get a cold and aren't as productive at work as you normally would be. On top of that, you have to miss your scheduled spin class. You go to a birthday party and have cake and a glass or two of wine. You go on a weekend getaway and forget to bring your vitamins. You're tired and aren't up for having sex. You're angry when your neighbor complains about motherhood. Perfectionism wants you to believe these normal human experiences mean, "You're not good enough." "You're not doing enough." "You're not ready to be a mom."

Fertility wants to pull you aside and say, "Perfectionism has been giving you false orders. You don't have to listen to it anymore. You don't have to feel ashamed for failing at a goal that isn't even possible to achieve. Hang with me and I promise, there's a better way to live."

Fertility wants to clarify something too. "You don't need to think positive thoughts or feel positive emotions 100 percent of the time to get pregnant. That's not necessary, nor is it humanly possible. I would never ask that of you."

The goal is not to be "happy" or "cheerful" 24/7. It *really* isn't. The goal is to feel the emotions that arise inside of your body and to not shame or *become* them. To allow space for all the emotions you feel—positive and negative alike—without judging yourself for having feelings. To meet yourself where you're at. To welcome emotions instead of shoving them away. For however long they need to be felt. And to understand the difference between pain (a necessary, natural, and healthy response to something hard to experience in life) and suffering (unnecessary levels of distress that your mind conjures up).

You would never say to your future child, "Be happy every minute of your life and never allow a negative thought to enter your mind because if you do, you're weak and not disciplined enough." And yet, that's essentially what we say to ourselves.

On your fertility journey, you don't need to think positive thoughts with unwavering perfection. You can, however, choose self-compassionate thoughts and speak kindly to yourself most (or at least some) of the time, and that is enough. That is all any human being can do. That is all Fertility wishes for you.

And if you really begin to out perfectionism's bullshit orders, you might even notice, like my client Alyssa, that there is another side of you waiting to be discovered.

ALYSSA'S STORY

All my life, I have been rewarded for being a hard worker. I would set a goal, grind away, and achieve success. The future was mine to control because I could get anything I wanted if I worked hard enough. I figured that getting pregnant would be no different.

When we started trying to get pregnant, and it didn't happen immediately, I felt disappointed, like I was already failing. When we lost our first baby just before hitting the second trimester, I was heartbroken and wondered if I had done something wrong. After the miscarriage, we tried for another year. My dream of holding a baby began to feel further and further away. As each month passed, and still no baby, I went deeper into my spiral of pain and shame.

Rather than processing my grief, I threw myself into my work at the real estate business I run with my husband: more clients, more listings, more sales. If I stayed super busy and productive, filling every waking moment with activities, I wouldn't have to feel my emotions.

I joined Spenser's program and met women who shared my dreams and struggles. I had an epiphany through conversations with Spenser and the other women in the group.

Striving for perfection leads me further away from my dreams, not closer.

Chasing perfection in my work (and all areas of my life) was not helping me conceive. All the hustling was putting my body into a state of chronic stress and blocking my baby from finding me. I needed to change the pattern.

It started with setting boundaries at work. Being an entrepreneur, I'd always been 100 percent committed to the business. I was plugged in 24/7 and never fully stepped away, not even on nights, weekends, or vacations. I began to silence my notifications so I wasn't jumping at every call, text, or email, creating quieter space in my day. When everything didn't crumble to the ground as I stepped away (surprise, surprise!), I began to trust that the Universe had my back.

Now that I wasn't interrupted by incoming messages all day and night, my brain had more space to consider, "What brings me joy?" I got curious about this question and discovered I longed to get messy! Pottery, painting, building something with my hands...I wanted to make something. There was a lighter, playful side of me who wanted to come out; a part of my personality I'd always silenced in the past.

A piece of my mind resisted: "You're not a painter! That's not a productive use of your time. What if you spend hours making artwork, and don't even like it once it's finished? Then you'll have nothing to show for it! You have more important things you ought to be doing."

I had to shut my mind up and tell myself, "It doesn't matter. I don't need to create a masterpiece. It's okay to do something purely for the joy of it."

I found a painting tutorial on YouTube, followed it, added my flair, and hung it proudly on my wall. For me, this was more than just a painting. It was a reminder to slow down, soften, and enjoy the journey, not just the end result.

Just before I got pregnant with my daughter, I was listening to one of Spenser's meditations. I usually take meditation very seriously. You know how most meditation teachers say, "When a thought enters your mind, clear it out, keep your mind completely blank, and focus on nothing." I always strived to keep my mind perfectly blank and (of course) felt frustrated when I inevitably failed.

But this time was different. I closed my eyes and listened to the guided meditation about my womb that Spenser has inside her program. Instead of forcing myself to remain blank, I visualized meeting my baby. Images appeared, and it was a full-blown disco party in my mind! I saw myself, my husband, and my baby dancing to some of my favorite jams, with furry fuchsia walls, a giant disco ball in the center, and sparkling reflections everywhere. My mind exploded with joy, color, messiness, and life.

During that meditation, I felt a decisive shift in my body, and I knew my old pattern of striving, hustling, and grasping was ending. And I knew: I need to mother and love myself as much as I long to mother and love my future baby.

Two weeks later, I had a positive pregnancy test. I believe my daughter was forming inside my body when I visualized our family dancing beneath the glittering disco ball.

Our minds have a funny way of reverting to things we're comfortable with. Now that I'm a mother (and currently pregnant with my second child), I've had moments where I felt pulled back into old patterns of perfectionism. But now, that perfection feels so stiff and uncomfortable. It no longer fits. The less I hustle, the more I feel peace and pleasure in my body. That's the path I will keep following and the example I will set for my children.

THE WIZARD BEHIND THE CURTAIN

Like Alyssa and many of the wise women I've worked with, I spent years hidden and trapped in the loopy lie of perfectionism. One day, while immersed in a journaling session, a vision from *The Wizard of Oz* washed over me.

Remember the scene when Dorothy meets the Great and Powerful Oz? Like everyone else in the kingdom, she believes the Wizard is all-knowing and all-powerful. He, and he alone, can make her dream come true.

More than anything, Dorothy just wants to go home. The Wizard promises he'll grant her wish, but first, she must prove she's worthy. How? By bringing him the broom of the Wicked Witch of the West. An almost impossible task.

When she finally gets him what he wants, he stalls and tells her to come back tomorrow, and that's when he will finally reward her.

Dorothy is frustrated, and her dog Toto goes behind the curtain to unveil the truth. Who is the Wizard of Oz? He is just a sad, insecure older man who has been tricking people into following his commands with smoke and mirrors. But it's all just theatrics. It's not real. He's not a wizard at all.[16]

Perfectionism is like the wizard behind the curtain.

Perfectionism says, "There's something you want more than anything? Only I can give it to you. But first, you must go on a challenging quest. Follow my instructions perfectly with absolutely no errors. If somehow you can succeed, then and only then, I'll give you what you want."

But even if you complete the quest, perfectionism lies to you again.

"Oh, it's not time for your reward just yet." "There's one more thing you need to do first." "Um, come back tomorrow!"

Like the Great and Powerful Oz, the last thing perfectionism will ever give you is what you want and what it has promised. *Perfectionism is a moving target.*

One client described it beautifully when she said, "Just when I check off all ten things on my fertility to-do list, an eleventh one pops up just as the day's coming to an end." Just when you think that, at long last, you have succeeded, perfectionism switches up the game and changes the rules. Its design does not lead you to your dreams but to dehydrate you from a feeling of enough-ness.

Perfectionism is a video game with no winning level.

Picture this: It's two o'clock in the morning, your hair is an oily mess, and you can't take your eyes off the screen, trying desperately to find out how to win this damn video game. But the secret is, there is no way to win. No matter how many new tricks you learn, or how much time you devote, you will never be rewarded because there's no winning level programmed into the game. Do you want to know the only way to win at the game of perfectionism? Stop fuckin' playing.

What choice do you have? You can continue taking orders from perfectionism. You can keep fighting to perfect your body, emotions, and actions. If that's the path you want to go down, that's your prerogative.

Or, you can remember you have options. You can stop playing the unwinnable game. You can stop taking orders from the sad man behind the curtain. You can recognize you don't need approval from the so-called Great and Powerful Wizard...who isn't even a wizard.

When you tell yourself, "I'm not doing enough to get pregnant; I need to do more and do it better...," you're only engaging in a boring game of perfectionism.

When you tell yourself with newfound confidence, "I'm the one who gets to decide when I'm doing enough. I can have good things in life even though I'm not perfect. Because no one is," perfectionism gets bored with you and eventually dies off.

The only one who can impregnate your mind and body with the rolling wave of relief that *you're doing enough* and that *you're safe to spend time living in and loving your current life* is you. You get to decide what *enough* means for you. Not culture. Not God. Not a positive pregnancy test. Not even your baby can give this to you. There is no one screaming hotter or colder. Because enough-ness is not dependent on what you did or didn't do the day before—this realization changed *everything* for me.

I couldn't wait anymore for that positive pregnancy test to tell me I was doing enough. Because I intuitively felt the only way my baby would come was if my worth weren't dependent on their arrival. I had to make this internal change *before* seeing those two pink lines.

The standards that culture, the fertility industry, and perfectionism have set up are dull, life-sucking, guarded, and restrictive. Pregnancy, the energy you want more than anything, is exciting, life giving, vulnerable, and expansive. The goal is to get close to that kind of energy. Not just to get pregnant but because you *choose* that for your life. You genuinely want that over the latter.

Fertility wants you to un-shame your humanity to see yourself as whole...now. She's here to tell you, "The wholeness of who you are *includes* your imperfections. I respectfully *don't care* if you complete your fertility to-do list. My energy being present and swirling around in your body depends not on what you *do*, but on who you are *being*. Because when you shift into a being state, you see me. You notice me. You feel me. You need to know I see your worth of a big, beautiful, baby-filled life right now. Today. I always have. Now, it's time to see and embody it for yourself."

You'd never want to shame your child for being beautifully, messily, and imperfectly human. Can you extend that same grace and compassion to yourself?

An exposing exercise is asking your perfectionist brain to tell you what you need to do to get pregnant. And to notice the tight, boring, and extremely high standards perfectionism places on you.

It helps to grab your pen and paper and ask your perfectionist brain to get more specific about the task to "out" the impossibility of your request.

Imagine if your perfectionist brain tells you to "eat healthy" or "stick to a clean meal plan." Follow up by asking, "Okay, perfectionist brain, what does that look like exactly? Never eat a french fry again until I push out that baby? Only eat a diet of protein and organic fruits and vegetables, even when my best friend is hosting an Italian dinner party? Work out eight times a week? Meditate for forty-five minutes daily?" By asking your perfectionistic brain to give specific details, you become aware of the impossibility behind the ask.

It's time to start questioning the "shoulds" *instead of yourself.* How many of these tasks are "shoulds" as opposed to genuine attraction and desire?

How many of these to-dos are actually in alignment with your nature?

Most importantly, are you leaving room to be a human?

What do you love to do that may not be approved by the (boring, stodgy, stuck-in-the-past) fertility industry but makes you so insanely happy?

Can you let yourself have it?

FEEL IT ALL OR FEEL NOTHING

Perfectionism slaps a big no-no on any feeling that dips below pure positivity, high hope, or any emotions labeled "negative."

However, this doesn't work on the fertility journey because it includes an entire cascade of emotions.

Many women I work with have highly sensitive nervous systems. They, as do I, feel things deeply. The acceptance of highly sensitive people has recently become so mainstream they gave us an acronym: HSP.

Being highly sensitive can be a gift. For example, when I look at a sunset, I am in awe over the bright, warm colors, the feeling that the warm, dewy temperature leaves on my body, and the gratitude for having the eyes to see it. I'll look over at everyone else, and they think the sunsets are cool and all, but then quickly get back to whatever they were doing.

When I watch the news or see someone I love in pain, it crushes me, sometimes to the point of nausea. I feel as if it's happening to me. Everyone else seems to "get over it" much quicker. I don't.

Whether they identify as HSP or not, all the TTC women I have worked with naturally and effortlessly love deeply and want to learn how to live with an open heart. But doing so requires an acceptance of both sides of the coin. To feel extraordinary joy, love, and pleasure, we also have to be willing to feel disappointment, sadness, and pain. We can't do selective mind–body numbing and feel certain emotions and not others. Our bodies just don't work that way. It's the price you pay to be alive! (I'll take it.) When you run away from one emotion, you run away from them all.

We must feel everything in life, including pain, or nothing
at all.

Which would you prefer?

EMOTIONS ARE NOT DANGEROUS

At a young age, we're told to "stop crying," to "be happy," and to
"stop being so sensitive," which only encourages us to live from
the neck up, stuck in our heads and disconnected from what
we instinctively want to feel inside our bodies.

We're scared of deep emotions like pain because we fear it
will last forever. "If I let this feeling in, it won't leave." On a
primal level, we might even think, *If I allow myself to feel pain,
I won't be able to stand it. I'll die.*

And so, when we experience pain, the nervous system reacts
to protect us. While these reactions are normal and natural and
exist to protect us, they tend to bring us further away from the
life we truly want.

FIGHT RESPONSE

When a threat is perceived emotionally or physically, your
nervous system may enter the fight response. You're ready to
confront the threat aggressively—scream, punch, go to war.
Physical signs include increased heart rate, rapid breathing,
and a release of the adrenaline hormone.

FLIGHT RESPONSE

At other times, your nervous system may swing into the flight response. Your body tries to help you escape the perceived threat and move away from the danger as fast as possible. Physical signs include heightened alertness and a readiness to move or flee.

FREEZE RESPONSE

The freeze response involves a temporary immobilization or "deer in the headlights" reaction when confronted with a threat. It's characterized as a slowing down of a physiological process and feeling stuck or unable to react. Physical signs are a reduced heart rate, shallow breathing, and feeling frozen in place.

FAWN RESPONSE

This response includes an instinctual urge to appease or please others when someone feels threatened. Physical signs include anxiety, a tendency to become overly accommodating, or a desire to avoid confrontation.

Knowing the different responses helps us get to know pain better. To not fear it but to better understand how it (and your body) works.

"I SHOULDN'T FEEL THIS WAY..."

When your nervous system is activated, and you're experiencing fight, flight, freeze, or fawn, what makes it so much harder is telling yourself the shame-filled response of, "I shouldn't be feeling this way."

But you *do* feel this way. That is the present-moment reality, and it's okay. The more you command yourself to "stop feeling this way," the more you keep the pain locked up inside of you, and it remains there for longer than it ordinarily would. The more we deny what we feel or place shame upon what we feel, the more those feelings get lodged in our cells.

Processing our deeper, darker, culturally ashamed emotions is not a skill that is taught or valued in our culture, although it is a very important one for living a long, healthy life. No wonder so many of us struggle to do this.

Pain is inevitable. Suffering, on the other hand, is optional. Suffering is what happens when we resist feeling the pain in our bodies, so we stay stuck in the mental story attached to the pain inside our heads. Culturally, it's much more common to ruminate in the mental story in our heads than to feel the physical sensations in our bodies.

Fertility wants you to know: I get that all of this is new and scary. But you need to know that emotions aren't dangerous.

At first, you might anticipate a tsunami of emotions. But the key is to *slowly* build internal safety to gently and tenderly move through your pain. Your body is built for this.

EVERY FEELING IS A VISITOR

The spiritual teacher Mooji said, "Feelings are just visitors. Let them come and go."

Of course, experiencing intrusive thoughts and emotions isn't a desirable experience. It's not fun to feel. But like observing clouds in the sky, you can allow them to come and go freely. Most will visit for a brief moment and then depart. Each one arrives for a reason, and you don't need to know that reason.

You might have certain visitors you prefer more than others (I know I do). Even so, when a visitor knocks, let her in, no matter who she may be. She's only here for a short visit.

Remember this when you're TTC and experiencing the pain of waiting, the pain of disappointment, and the pain of loss.

Remember this when you're in labor and having contractions.

Remember this, too, once you're rocking your precious baby in your arms, sleep-deprived and overwhelmed.

Like my client Robin, no matter how intense the emotion feels inside your body, it's a visitor. All it wants is to be allowed and felt. You have everything you need to slowly build the capacity to experience, honor, and let it go.

ROBIN'S STORY

My fertility struggles have been raw, messy, and uncomfortable as hell. It has more than rocked my boat. It has capsized the ship and left me adrift, lost, in the deepest pain. One day, I hope I'll be able to say that this challenge has been the "best thing that ever happened to me," but I'm not there yet. At the same time, I've gained invaluable gifts from my fertility journey.

After our fourth transfer, resulting in our third chemical pregnancy, I had a conversation with another woman whom I met through Spenser's program. I told her, "I feel so sad saying goodbye to this last baby and all of my babies." It hurts. I have uncontrollable tears when I think to myself, I may never have a child. In the past, this pain would consume every part of my being and fill every waking minute of the day. But now, I don't grip the pain so tightly. I can experience it, honor it, and let it go. It's still there and will probably always be there, but there's a softness instead of the hardness I used to feel.

Through working with Spenser, I've gained the ability to slow down, feel how I feel, and truly rest. I was living my life so hard in the past, and I was constantly in fast mode. Everything was a transaction, a means to an end. I was not present in my life or my body. Today, I'm more aware of when I need to pause. Recently, I took a sick day off work and stayed home. Not because I was violently ill but simply because I felt low energy and wanted to rest. The "old me" would never have done this!

Previously, my worthiness was contingent on what I could produce. I felt I needed to be in high–production mode at work and needed to produce a baby too. I've worked on dismantling these old beliefs and building new ones to stand in their place. "I am enough." "I find safety in everything I do." "My fertility journey is going to end up even better than I thought." And my personal favorite: "I attract good things like a fucking magnet!" New thoughts play in my mind on repeat. It has brought me so much relief.

As I type this story, I am not pregnant. I have waited years for my child to arrive, and it hasn't happened. And yet, I feel calm. I have a sense of peace about my life. I feel gratitude for everything I have now and desire more. I've learned I can experience gratitude and desire simultaneously. Both/and. I never imagined I could feel this way, and it's been a long road to get here.

My life is beautiful, not because I'm holding my baby, not yet. It's beautiful because I found my own worth.

PAIN IS A PORTAL

As you see in Robin's story, the bravery she built and the willingness to feel her pain naturally created this by-product of worthiness within her and a "If I can get through this, I can get through anything" kind of confidence.

She will certainly carry forth this life experience and skill she now has in her mind–body tool kit to her future children.

Glennon Doyle Melton, author of one of my favorite books, *Untamed*, appeared on Oprah's *Super Soul Sunday*. A woman in the audience said to Glennon, "I want to do everything in my power to prevent my child from feeling pain." Glennon said, "What other qualities do you want your child to have?" The woman said, "I want my son to become kind, wise, and resilient."

Glennon said, "Okay then, what is it in life that creates kindness, wisdom, and resilience? It's pain. It's not having nothing to overcome. It's overcoming and overcoming and overcoming. So is it possible we are trying to protect our children from the one thing that will allow them to become the people we dream they'll be?"

The same is true for you.

Like Robin, your pain is your portal to greater kindness, wisdom, and resilience. It's an opening to build compassion and fuel the world with more vulnerability and empathy. It's not something to bypass or avoid.

When we assure ourselves, "I'm safe to feel pain; it's uncomfortable, but it's temporary," we paradoxically open our hearts to everything we want.

When you close your heart off to pain, you inadvertently close yourself off to pleasure. The heart is the birthplace of all emotions—the ones you enjoy and those you don't particularly prefer.

If you believe that finally getting pregnant is going to be one of the most pleasurable experiences of your life, but you won't let your body experience and process the pain that shows up in your life, you unconsciously close your heart off to both.

The ancient wisdom in Chinese medicine shares that a channel called the *Bao Mai* connects your heart to your womb.

An open heart equals an open womb. You must be willing to experience both.

YOU'RE TEACHING YOUR BABY...RIGHT NOW

The month before I got pregnant with my first child, I went out for a girls' night and one of the women was randomly so rude to me. I have no idea what I did to offend her (*maybe she had one too many margaritas*), but she was comin' at me the entire night with plenty of eye rolls and snide comments. She must have been going through something hard. It really triggered me and brought back painful memories of my junior high days, being bullied and mistreated. When I left the restaurant, I was shaking.

I used to shame the hell out of myself for getting triggered.

"I'm not supposed to feel this way. I can't afford to be upset because it's not good for my fertility. Ugh, I'm so sensitive."

But this time was different. I remember responding to myself with such love and empathy.

"I'm allowed to feel this way because—reality check—*I feel this way.* I'm not making my humanity wrong anymore. I'm going to take some time to be confused and sad. And I want to teach my future child to do the same."

Life isn't automatically beautiful. We make it beautiful when we meet ourselves exactly where we're at.

One thing I share with clients—especially those who are newly pregnant and feel wrong to feel anything but excitement and gratitude at all waking moments of the day when in reality they're anxious and puking their guts out—is this:

The spirit of your baby doesn't want to come into a life expecting to be, feel, and do everything perfectly. They want the freedom to explore all the different colors of being alive.

Every time you feel scared, you tell your baby s/he is allowed to feel scared. Whenever you listen to anger and set a boundary, you give your future baby permission to do the same. Every time you feel pleasure, your baby now knows this essence of joy will be a part of their life too.

Your spiritual beliefs may be different from mine, and that's okay. I believe your baby is near you right now, watching and learning, absorbing the lessons you provide simply by choosing to live an authentically imperfect life. As you move forward on your fertility journey, let your choices show your baby, "This is what it means to be human." "This is how we feel our emotions." "This is okay." "This is safe." "This is life. It's messy, unorganized, it's not perfect, and it's still so amazing." "When you're here earthside, and you're having a hard moment, I'll hold you, rock you, and remind you it's okay to be human. I'll wrap you up in love, just like I'm doing for myself."

A TINY SPARK OF HOPE

After several years of trying and trying (and trying!) for a baby, it becomes a hardwired habit to automatically anticipate getting your period versus getting pregnant.

About a week before my period was due to arrive, I'd begin bracing myself for impact.

"I barely worked out this month, so there's no way I'll be pregnant."

"My emotions have been all over the place. I need to better control my feelings and think more positively. I'm out this month."

And even, "I had a bit of a cold last week, so there's no way it could happen."

It didn't matter how good of a girl I was and how disciplined I was 90 percent of the time; if I wasn't perfect, I wasn't good enough to get pregnant. (Or so I believed back then.)

Expecting the worst became my comfort zone. A familiar place. A state I subconsciously chose so I could predict and have control over it, even though it's not what I consciously would have selected. I did this because I didn't feel safe opening my heart and risking feeling pain. It was easier and more comfortable to assume it didn't work and wouldn't work. Sitting in the uncertainty of not knowing was just too much.

ALL-OR-NOTHING THINKING

One of the characteristics of perfectionism is *all-or-nothing thinking*. It's viewing situations, events, or your own experiences and emotions in extreme terms with no middle ground or shades of gray. With all-or-nothing thinking, you see things as either entirely good, or more often than that, altogether bad. Anything less than 100 percent is considered a failure.

So if you're not high on hopefulness (coupled with a hormone-free diet) every minute of every day, then you internally register, anticipate, and prepare for that month to not work out.

By automatically assuming "I was out this month," I kept myself shielded from good things in life as well. Because we've learned that when we block pain, we block pleasure too.

Gradually, I realized I needed to take down the shield. I had to do the bravest thing of all: allow myself to feel a tiny spark of hope for a baby again. To open my heart once again.

There's a life coach I admire and have worked with named Susan Hyatt. Once, a client said to Susan, "There's something I really want but I'm afraid to get my hopes up." Susan replied, "Get your hopes up." She assured her client, "You are strong enough to handle all the emotions that arise—the joy when you get exactly what you want, the disappointment if you don't, and everything in between." You were built to handle it all.

When we think of courage, we think of battles, ferocity, iron will, and toughness. But quietly opening up your heart to feel a tiny spark of hope is the most courageous act of all.

CAN YOU DO NINETY SECONDS?

The thoughts of the mind translate to feelings in the body. What creates a mind–body connection is reopening the channels between these two destined partners. It's allowing the mind and body to exchange, filter, and move out the energy that's actively and undeniably in motion. These two are meant to work together. Like a seed needs sunlight. That's the original natural design.

All emotions have a purpose. Anger encourages you to create boundaries. Sadness illuminates what you value most. Grief shows you how much love you're capable of experiencing. Frustration could be an invitation to cultivate more present-moment patience. Instead of seeing your emotions as either good or bad, know that they all serve a purpose.

The word "emotions" is often broken down into "e-motion" to emphasize the idea that emotions are, in a sense, "energy in motion" or "movements of energy" within the body and mind.

Dr. Jill Bolte Taylor is a Harvard-trained neuroscientist. One day, she had a stroke, and a major hemorrhage on the left half of her brain—the analytical, thinking side—made it go offline. She could not walk, talk, read, write, or recall any of her life. All she could do was feel and sense energy.

While in this state, she made an incredible discovery: most emotions (when completely allowed to exist without resistance) only last for ninety seconds. They arrive, they reach a peak, then dissipate, and depart. There's a ninety-second arc and then the emotion, whatever it may be—anger, sorrow, grief—begins to subside.

To clarify, this doesn't mean you finish grieving in ninety seconds and then you're all done and never feel grief again. What it means is, the most intense part of the emotion—the part that's really hard—is only ninety seconds long and then you get a break before another wave may (or may not) come in. It's much like a contraction during labor. There's intensity followed by a rest so you can recover.

I can do anything for ninety seconds. So can you.

HOW TO ACTUALLY FEEL

Fertility wants you to know: It's safe to feel your feelings. It's safe to feel pain. It's safe to feel hope. And it's safe to feel everything in between.

But how do you actually do this? In school, you're taught how to read, write, and solve math problems. But who teaches you how to feel safe experiencing sensations in your body and how to process your emotions?

Let's start with pain, since this is the emotion we resist the most. Opening your heart to pain is not a task you can check off your to-do list. It requires presence to know you can feel an unexpected wave of sadness and heartache that is asking to come through, and all it's asking is to be felt.

When we experience pain, we often think, *Why is this happening? Where is this coming from? When will this feeling go away? What can I do to make it go away?* We go to a therapist seeking answers. We get a psychological report. We pore over the details of the past—family, high school, medical, and dating history—to put all the pieces together as to why this pain is coming up now. I mean no disrespect to therapists or any healing profession, but here's the thing: it doesn't really matter why it's there. What your pain wants more than anything is simply to be acknowledged. It doesn't necessarily want to be analyzed or explained. It wants to be seen, felt, and heard, just like every other part of you.

As you will see in Daisy's story, a well-lived, meaningful life, one with fulfilling adventures, self-trust, and the ability to surrender to all the twists and turns in your life, includes pain, and this is not a problem.

DAISY'S STORY

While trying to get pregnant, I was overwhelmed by compulsive, spiraling thoughts about my infertility. I didn't understand why my body wasn't doing what it was supposed to do. On particularly bad days, I hid in the bathroom at work and wept uncontrollably. At night, I'd scroll online for hours trying to find stories like mine, going down rabbit holes of various diagnoses, hunting for answers to: "What am I doing wrong?"

I did acupuncture, and reflexology, overhauled my diet to cut out sugar, gluten, and alcohol, saw countless specialists, and nothing worked. After appointments, I'd cry on the way home. I felt like I was failing despite all my efforts.

When I connected with Spenser and met the wonderful, kind women in her program, it felt like a fog slowly lifting. My shame lifted, too, especially after hearing the other women share their stories. They were so honest and vulnerable, and so like me.

Two months after beginning my work with Spenser, I had a miscarriage. She created a space where I could feel my grief, find a way to honor the loss and be less alone.

Shortly after my miscarriage, a friend came to stay for the weekend and told me, "I'm pregnant." During her visit, I excused myself for a moment and did a brief meditation that was included in the program. I breathed, cried, and felt the strong emotions pulsing through me. I surrendered to the experience instead of pushing my feelings away. Afterward, I returned to my friend and was able to celebrate her joyful news. I could feel the bittersweet tinge of jealousy and sadness but without becoming it.

Spenser encouraged me to look for signs from the Universe that my baby was near. I began seeing purple flowers everywhere, blooming on my walks, and felt my heart expand each time I spotted them. With the group's support, I began to ask for help, be gentler to myself, and accept what is rather than manically controlling every part of my life. I was blooming too.

My husband and I went through a difficult time, got counseling, and ultimately separated. As our marriage ended, I got pregnant. My time as a mother has not been straightforward. I moved back to my parents' house, quit my job, put my house up for sale, and came to terms with unexpectedly being a single parent. I have cried my eyes out in the long dark nights of the soul.

This isn't the version of motherhood I expected. And, it is a kaleidoscope of loveliness, tiredness, overwhelm, love, joy, worry, and wondering. I don't have all the answers. I don't know what the future holds. But I know I was chosen to be a mother to Matthew, and it is the honor of my life to continue to walk beside him in this world of ours. Together, we look for four-leaf clovers, swim, eat ice cream, visit the cinema, and see friends. The best of all: holding hands as we nap together.

My fertility journey isn't yet over. I feel I have one more spirit baby waiting in the wings. I'm excited to see what unfolds in the next chapter. No matter what, I trust myself to know the next right step.

When Daisy first began feeling how she really felt, it was odd at first. Like a baby learning to walk, she had to experiment with different modalities of mind–body medicine. But eventually, she found ways that worked *for her*.

When you experience an emotion, from hope that you're not used to feeling to pain that you've been pushing down, here's a simple way to feel it. Don't deny it. Don't shame it. Don't push it away. Actually feel it. This may feel messy, unorganized, and unpredictable at first (just like parenting) but it gets easier with time.

MIND–BODY EXERCISE: MEETING YOUR PAIN

In my imagination, I see myself sitting under a big, beautiful, drooping tree—like a willow tree—and it feels like a safe, comfortable place to feel a new emotion, and new is almost always odd at first.

On a side note, I remember spending so much of my childhood climbing trees, so this makes sense that it's where I feel at home. Feel free to change your scenery to a landscape that feels most like home to you.

Notice the Mental Story

Become aware of the story that's coming up. That one on repeat that keeps rearing its old head. "I shouldn't feel this way because..." "I'm not there yet because..." Or maybe it's an old memory that seems to come out of nowhere.

Notice the Emotions

Now see how the mental story is creating an emotional experience in your body. Where in the body do you feel it? Is it in your chest, your stomach, your throat? For a moment, even if it's only for five seconds, drop the mental story. Come into your body and focus on your breath. Breathe into the physical sensations in your body. Try to let go of any commentary about your pain, like, "It's good that I feel this...," or "It's bad that I feel this..." Set the mental story aside. Bring your attention to sensations in your body, not words in your head.

Let Go of Needing to Fix It

If you believe that pain isn't inherently bad, then you can also stop seeing it as a problem that needs to go away as fast as possible. Let it be there. Let it be acknowledged. You can speak to your pain as if it's a visitor. "Oh, hey it's you again. I'll say hi to you by letting you be here inside of my body."

When you stop needing to push your pain out of the body, and instead allow for its presence, this creates the space it needs to eventually move through you. This is a big irony. The more we accept pain and even welcome it inside, the faster it tends to depart.

Know that the feeling or emotion may last longer than ninety seconds. Let go of your perfectionism. Take it slow. Give it time.

It's easy to get caught in the act of using every healing modality known to man to make it move through you faster. This pressure is not only from you but from loved ones who don't like seeing you in pain. But you must know that if meditation, journaling, a walk, or communicating about how you feel doesn't seem to make it go away, then that's okay too. It's not meant to be overcome as fast as possible. Allowing emotions to move slowly creates an immense amount of safety for your mind and body.

If no matter what you do, it's still there, it's asking to stay there and be felt. That's what it needs.

CHAPTER SUMMARY

1. You are safe to let go of perfectionism. It's a moving target. A game with no winning level. It's time to stop playing, Mama Bear.

2. There is no one screaming "hotter" or "colder" on the journey to your baby. The only one who can fill you with a feeling of worthiness is you.

3. High vibes and happiness all the time is not the path to conception. Cultivating compassion for your humanity and learning how to nurture your imperfections is far more effective in eliminating shame and creating ease, flow, and openness within your mind and body connection.

4. Emotions are not dangerous. You were designed to feel the full spectrum of emotion—pain, pleasure, and everything in between. This practice of feeling how you really feel is what opens your heart (and your womb) to your baby.

5. You're teaching your baby right now. By releasing perfectionism and responding to yourself with understanding and acceptance of what it's like to be a human being, you inadvertently teach your baby the same: "You don't have to be perfect to be deeply and completely loved."

CHAPTER 4

MEET YOURSELF AGAIN

THE PRESSURE TO MAKE IT HAPPEN

The desire to have a baby was planted in your heart for a reason. You would be doing a disservice to yourself if you didn't listen to the call. But it's helpful to explore why you might feel so much pressure to make it happen beyond the congruent desire to have a baby and raise a family.

Society places immense pressure on women to conceive, to fit into the box of "what's normal," and to reproduce by a certain age. The external pressure is real and just as alive as your yearning to conceive.

A good chunk of the unnecessary suffering you're experiencing might be because of the rush you feel to get the world off your damn back.

The never-ending questions ("So when are you having a baby?") or the random, intrusive recommendations ("Remember to lift your feet up after sex!") feel awkward and condescending.

It might feel like the only solution to make these questions and comments go away is to just get pregnant. This creates even more pressure to conceive and do it fast.

One of my clients, Grace, was a part of a huge girlfriend group chat. Every time she would hear a ping sound on her phone, her heart would drop into her stomach. Either they were talking about something cute their baby did that day or it was another one of those happy-for-her-but-sad-for-me pregnancy announcements.

The social pressure to keep up with her group of girlfriends made her mind race a mile a minute. She felt left behind and unimportant compared to her friends who were already moms.

GRACE'S STORY

Before working with Spenser, I completely alienated myself socially, especially from my closest friends. It seemed like their lives were moving on because they were getting pregnant easily and having kids. In my mind, they had it all while I had a gaping hole in my life. I hated living in a silent home with just my husband and me because I craved the noise, chaos, and love of a house full of children. I work as a teacher, surrounded by children all day long, which made the ache even worse.

At my lowest point, I muted my closest friends on social media so I wouldn't feel the painful pang every time they shared photos of their children and picture-perfect lives. It was agonizing to look at the "Mum Club" that I so desperately wanted to join.

Working with Spenser, I gently unpacked the stories I'd been telling myself. I realized, "I have attached my self-worth to being a mom. I've convinced myself that if I don't have a baby, then I'm not worthy of friendship, love, and acceptance."

Once I felt safe enough to trust myself, I realized the feeling of "them" (people with children) and "me" was just a story that fear and doubt had created. They are still them, as they were before children, and I am still me. Our relationship hasn't changed; just what I had been telling myself about it had. I was able to see how amazing my life was, baby or not. Just because we were on our journey to our baby didn't mean life was any different from the way it was before. I was and am worthy because I always have been.

As I type this, I am pregnant with my second child. I conceived my first through IVF while I was in Spenser's program and my second naturally. Neither path is necessarily better or worse, just different, and both can be empowering.

Taking this approach to my baby has shifted my whole life from just existing in fear and doubt to fully living in presence, peace, and love. It truly was a journey back to my authentic self, peeling away every layer the fertility journey had built up.

A WOMAN'S WORTH

At the time I'm writing this book, *Barbie* has made over a billion bucks at the box office. Women around the world are so moved by the messages in this movie.

There's a speech that made millions of women cry, as America Ferrera's character talks about how impossible it is for women to live up to society's standards: "It is literally impossible to be a woman," she declares. "We have to always be extraordinary, but somehow we're always doing it wrong."

You have to be thin, but not too thin. Strong and fit, too, but not too muscular. Successful, but not intimidatingly so. Financially secure, but not overly focused on money. Powerful, but not so powerful that others feel inferior in your presence. Confident, but never boasting about your achievements. Appealing to men, but without needing or wanting their approval. And of course, everything is always your fault. It's because you wore that inappropriately short skirt or because you weren't home enough, weren't loving or perfect enough.

All of these impossible-to-reach standards. Whether you're TTC ("No kids yet? Why not? Don't you want kids?"), or a stay-at-home mom ("Wow, no career, really? And you call yourself a feminist?"), work part time ("Guess she's not very ambitious"), work full time ("Those poor kids, they must never see their mom"), and you're judged no matter what. Regardless of what you do, someone is only too happy to tell you, "You're doing it wrong." You can't win.

The social pressure to fit into the box of what's normal and acceptable is impossible. Because once you finally reach a societal point of success, the goalpost changes, and if you're honest, you realize you can't please everyone and you're judged either way. But more so, chasing society's definition of success is a distraction from designing a life that feels authentic and exciting to *you*.

When I decided to choose myself, what I wanted, and what I needed—even if it went against what society deemed as normal and acceptable for a woman of my age, education, sexual orientation, and marital status—it gave me the clues I needed that eventually took me to my baby.

When I quit working for my family's business and told everyone I was training to become a life coach, people looked at me as if I'd lost a few brain cells. "A life coach? What's that? Isn't it highly unlikely you'll earn a living doing that?" Nonetheless, I pursued this career path, regardless of people's concerns and reservations. This was the right call because it was *my call.* My new career fulfilled my need to feel purposeful even before my baby was here—and continues to be a source of rewarding excitement beyond motherhood.

Or when I chose not to do IVF for the first few years TTC and instead embarked on a spiritual journey of self-discovery. Many, including my husband, couldn't understand I was guided to a slower, different path. This journey fulfilled my desire to connect to magic and mystery that continues to make my life feel exciting, adventurous, and bold.

Or when I finally came up with an answer to the infamous question, "So when are you two finally gonna have kids?" A quick and confident reply of, "Soon!" A one-word explanation was more than good enough. It felt genuine and honest to me as I thought my baby was on the way, and the brief response usually disarmed any follow-up questions that people may have thought they were entitled to (when they weren't).

Or when I experienced a miscarriage and decided to talk about it. This was hard for my loved ones to hear. We aren't raised to speak about something so raw and vulnerable. It felt scary yet so freeing to tell my truth and liberate the perfectionist part of me that was taught to hide my pain and protect others from pain.

Or when people saw my husband and I thriving in our marriage and living a damn good life, even though we had been struggling for years to conceive. It was revolutionary for many of my online followers and the people in my life to see a couple who still hadn't gotten pregnant yet and decided they still see themselves worthy of a joyful life. Because circumstances don't create our happiness; our perception of it does.

Fertility wants you to know: The need for outside approval is a search that leads you away from the life you are meant to live and away from your innate and highly fertile nature. And ultimately, away from the life your child is meant to live, for he or she will be raised by the values instilled inside of you.

Here's a ridiculously simple yet life-altering question: *What do you actually want?*

Not your spouse or partner, not your parents, not your friends, not your Instagram followers, your colleagues, clients, your church, or neighbors. *You.* You might not know the answer just yet. If not, that's okay.

A successful woman is not the one who confirms society's impossible and ever-changing standards of perfection. It's the woman who does whatever the hell she wants.

TAKE THE BABY OFF THE PEDESTAL

Evolutionarily, our brains are wired to focus on immediate threats or concerns. Because if we didn't? Well, we'd die. In modern times, this can mean that our brains prioritize solving problems rather than focusing on gratitude or what we're pleased about.

It becomes a pattern of putting life on hold and repeatedly saying to ourselves, "I'll do what I want when XYZ happens."

The problem with this constant problem-solving approach to life is that it creates a feeling of stagnation, many missed opportunities, and an overall feeling of "I'm not *there* yet." (Even though "there" is arbitrary.) Feeling satisfied is the fuel we need to confidently move through life.

The biggest problem with problem-solving thinking is it puts the baby high on a pedestal.

"Once I have a baby," I assured myself, "*then* I'll live according to my values and teach my child to do the same. I'll have picnics in the park and carefree weekends at the lake. I'll spend less time on my phone and more time reading or out in nature. I'll quit my job and finally go after that dream career. I'll decorate the entire house for the holidays and host a big party. I'll have a purpose in life. I will..."

And so on. You get the idea. So many life goals but *only* once the baby gets here.

I didn't recognize it at the time, but I was placing my baby on an impossibly high pedestal. I was making the baby the most important thing on earth—more important than my own life. And I was attaching all my hopes and dreams to another person, making it their responsibility for me to be fulfilled.

Many of my clients do this too. We place an unreasonable amount of pressure on babies to make our lives whole.

I frequently tell the women in my programs, "You gotta take the baby off the pedestal."

Yes, your baby is a miracle. But you are a miracle too.

Sure, your baby will give you a new sense of purpose. But parenting is not necessarily your only purpose on earth. What else are you here to birth into this world?

Yes, your baby will bring you joy. But trust me, you'll need brief breaks from mamahood. And eventually, you'll become an empty nester. What will bring you joy now *and* then? Maybe it's hosting a Nancy-Meyers-movie-worthy dinner with friends, exploring a new hiking trail, or reading a sexy romance novel. You want your future child to witness you experiencing an abundant life independently, not turning to them as your sole source of happiness.

Yes, your baby will have the sweetest-smelling head, and the cuddliest cheeks, and their first smile will make you melt inside. Also, there will be many difficult nights when you're trying to nurse your newborn at 3:00 a.m., they're not latching correctly, your nipples are cracked and bleeding, you're wearing an adult-sized diaper and leaking postpartum fluids, you're so tired that you spontaneously start sobbing, and it's just really *hard*.

There's a difference between having a healthy desire for a child versus making the child your everything and the only thing that will complete your life.

If you're going to put somebody on a pedestal, put yourself up there. Celebrate the miracle of your own life, and your child will learn to do the same for themselves through the example you set.

RECLAIM YOUR POWER (AND LEARN WHAT'S THE RIGHT NEXT STEP FOR *YOU*)

The fertility journey is an opportunity to get to know yourself again. Your real self. Your nature. Not the one culture tells you you're supposed to be. The woman you really are. The mom you are meant to be.

I cannot tell you how often I've heard women say, "I'm doing everything I should be doing. I know I'm doing what I'm supposed to. I'm doing everything right; why am I not pregnant?"

"Should," "supposed to," and "have to" are all words from culture, societal pressure, and perfectionism. They make us feel powerless over our options and handcuffed to the demands of strangers on the internet, claiming they know what we need, even though they know nothing about us or what it's like to be on the fertility roller-coaster ride.

Whether you're about to embark on an IVF cycle or trying to conceive the good old-fashioned way, everything you're filling your day with—every appointment, vitamin, and meditation—is a choice.

"My doctor told me I have to do this type of treatment this cycle," I often hear from my clients.

"Really? You don't have a choice in this matter?" I ask.

"Well, I'm just listening to what they tell me to do," they respond.

"You say you have to do this kind of treatment. How does that make you feel?" I ask in return.

"Powerless. Handcuffed. Like I don't have a choice," they say with regret.

"You don't have to do anything. You always have a choice. If you decide to do this as per your doctor's recommendation, then it's a choice you make. You have full sovereignty over your body."

You don't have full control over your fertility journey, this is true. There's uncertainty, destiny, and mystery along the way (as there is in any worthy endeavor). However, in every moment, you always have a choice.

When clients realize this, the confidence that washes over them is visible. Their foreheads relax. Their shoulders settle. They take a deep sigh of relief. In the last two months, I've seen this specific shift help three women in my program get pregnant, after multiple failed cycles.

There's a big difference between asking for support versus giving all of your sovereignty and discernment to an outside source. You work in collaboration with the people you invite to be part of your fertility circle. There is no hierarchy.

When you connect to the baby compass inside of you and lean into what feels right and true to you within your mind, body, and spirit, you're taking back your power. You no longer feel like you're grasping at straws or throwing spaghetti at the wall to see what sticks.

My client Heather is a great example of this. After a failed IVF cycle, she was craving something new. She spoke to her doctor and expressed that she wanted to try something different. Intuitively, she sensed she needed fresh energy. Working with her doctor, they came up with a new plan which Heather considered and then said, "Okay, I choose to do this." Emphasis on the word *choose*. Unlike before, when she simply followed along with whatever she was told to do, this time, she embodied her new truth that it was her agreed choice. This new plan was successful. At the time I'm writing this book, she's four months pregnant.

Your language impacts your peace.

"I choose to..." are the three most empowering words you can use.

Ask yourself, "Who am I beyond my fertility journey?"

"Who do I choose to be, besides a mother?"

The answers to these questions are signposts to your baby, and to your needs that are wanting and patiently waiting to be fulfilled now. Mama Bear, it's time to fill *your* cup.

MIND-BODY MANTRA

Inside of every big desire, there is a need that wants to be met. A need for affection, belonging, excitement, purpose, or something else that you crave.

One hundred percent of the time, some aspect of this need can be met right now, even before you have a baby.

"I really want _____. I may not have it, yet, but right now I can meet this need by _____."

YOU ARE THE AUTHORITY

You are the highest authority on your body, including your reproductive system. You are the authority when it comes to conception, pregnancy, labor, and delivery. And you are the authority on motherhood in your household, because you will choose the values you want to instill into your child.

The problem is, when you're TTC and it's not working out, your confidence begins to erode. You question your instincts and second-guess your decisions. You worry that you're not the right person to lead this sacred mission. Somebody else—a doctor, a fertility expert—is better equipped for that role.

You don't trust yourself to make the right decisions. It's time to build that confidence, Mama Bear.

Before joining my program, my lovely client Ashley B. was living her life in accordance with society's (lame-ass) standards. She was dutifully acting out the part of "good girl" to gain outside validation and fit in with her family and friends. But she realized that when you do what everyone else does, it's like reading someone else's map. It leads to destinations you have no desire to visit. Despite diligently following the directions, you find yourself in places that are not your vibe and monotonous.

But once you learn how to read and follow your own map, all roads lead to a deeper feeling of "Ahhh, this feels so much better," which leads to more self-trust. Because when you have your own back, you know you're okay no matter what happens.

ASHLEY B.'S STORY

Like so many women, I spent many years living according to society's expectations. I wanted to fit in, make my family proud, and be the best wife I could be. I had a timeline of when certain benchmarks were supposed to happen—dating, engagement, marriage, and babies—according to TV shows and movies. When I wanted something, and it didn't work out, I blamed myself excessively and figured it was all my fault because I didn't try hard enough.

While I didn't recognize it at the time, my life was run by fear of judgment from others. I wasn't pausing to consider, "What do I actually want?" Or "What feels right to me?" Instead, my actions were determined by, "What will people think?"

When I started trying to have a baby, on the outside, I was putting on a good show, trying to be the perfect daughter, wife, and mama-to-be. But on the inside, I was miserable, fighting the urge to let my true feelings and thoughts rise to the surface, and desperately trying to keep it all together.

After connecting with Spenser, I learned how to feel my feelings. And oh, did I have some feelings to feel! Everything I'd been pressing down came to the surface. Spenser's group—with fellow women on the fertility journey—provided a space where I could say exactly what I felt (no matter how messy or painful) and simply be heard with no judgment.

Then I got pregnant for the first time and miscarried. My body ached, my mind raced, and I felt so lost. But I was exactly where I needed to be: surrounded by women who truly understood. I was given space to grieve and heal and even find the beauty beneath all the pain.

The sorrow I felt after my miscarriage was a catalyst for growth. Through my grief, I became more open with my family and allowed myself to be vulnerable at depths I'd never imagined. I learned to set boundaries, accept help from loved ones, and rest.

The main thing I want to share with women who are TTC is that it's okay to enjoy your life right now. Even if you're not pregnant yet, even if you don't get pregnant for another one or two years, your life is a miracle. On my journey, I gradually learned how to take the time to soak in the small moments of life and savor them. Having a baby is a blessing, and each day we're fortunate enough to be alive is a blessing too. It's easy to forget this. Every day we have an opportunity to remember.

I learned how to release the expectations for a fairy-tale life with a perfect timeline and focused on enjoying my imperfect life as it is. I attended our coaching calls with Spenser and fellow women to connect and share. I got coached. I wrote in my journal and meditated. I continued to open up to my family, sharing how I actually felt and not just what I thought people wanted to hear.

A few months later, I found out I was pregnant with my son.

When you don't get pregnant on the timeline you would prefer, it can be excruciatingly painful, but it's also an opportunity to grow as a woman. You acquire skills that you bring into your next chapter as a mom. Skills like listening to your instincts, taking better care of your mental and physical health, handling stress more effectively, communicating with the most important people in your life, and coping with grief.

If I hadn't gone through heartache and difficult lessons on my fertility journey, I wouldn't be the parent I am today.

I want to gently whisper to whoever is reading this, "Whatever you're going through is shaping you into the woman and mom you were meant to be." Some part of you, deep down, knows this is true.

SHAMEFUL MOTIVATION VERSUS COMPASSIONATE MOTIVATION

Like Ashley B., sometimes we feel compelled to do certain things in life—join a gym, go after a promotion at work, buy a home in a particular neighborhood, drive a certain car, have a baby in a certain way and on a certain timeline, and we're not even sure where this motivation comes from.

The next time you need to make a decision, ask yourself, "Is this something I truly want? Is this longing coming from my heart, my nature, my inner compass? Or is it blending with or maybe even rooted in shame, in an attempt to fit in?" How can you tell the difference?

There's a difference between shameful motivation and compassionate motivation. Here's an example you might relate to.

One choice we have at least three times per day is choosing what to eat.

SHAMEFUL MOTIVATION

Shame leads the internal mental dialogue by first making you feel as useless and as small as a tiny grain of old, rotting rice. As if the disgust it leaves inside of your body will somehow light a long-awaited fire under your ass. Hint: *It doesn't.*

"I've been too busy to cook healthy meals lately. I'm so lazy and bloated with this junk I've been eating. What's wrong with me? I need to step it up."

COMPASSIONATE MOTIVATION

Beginning with a type of motherly validation always paves the path for change.

Validation: "Yup. You're right. Things have been crazy at

work. It's not easy having a career and running a house. At times, it can be difficult to manage both."

Curiosity: "Eating well is a priority for me. I wanna feel good. I wonder, how can I make it a bit easier to do this? Oh ya! Grocery delivery! Or what about asking my partner to cook? And how about ordering in or going out on a date night once a week? Geez, this could be fun!"

Shameful motivation feels like a naggy feeling, a slap on the wrist, a bully reminding you that you're not good enough. It sounds like, "You're lazy." "You need to be more disciplined." "You never follow through consistently." "Other people handle this easily; why can't you?" Shame makes you feel inept at adulting. And remember, perfection is always riding shotgun.

Compassionate motivation feels curious, rested, grounded, and can even be fun. Compassion wants to guide you toward a solution that's easy to follow through with and makes the journey much more enjoyable.

You may think, *If I'm compassionate toward myself, then I'll become weak. I won't get anything done. I won't get what I want.* (Including a baby.)

Research shows the opposite is true.[17] As reported by BetterUp, one of the world's top organizations on behavioral change, people who are self-compassionate tend to have higher self-esteem and more resilience, be more willing to try again after a mistake or failure, and be more motivated to make positive changes in life. Compassion, it turns out, is a more powerful motivator than shame. In fact, it's the antidote. And it's one of the most powerful, medicinal mind–body tools we've got.

Fertility says, "Each time you're a bit more compassionate toward yourself, you move closer to the life you want, and you dissolve the barricade of shame that's been keeping you in hiding and isolation."

MIND–BODY EXERCISE: HOW TO
TRUST YOURSELF AGAIN

Take Time to Listen to What You Need.
Meet Yourself Where You're At.

For example, "My heart is hurting, and I'm starting to feel anxious. I need a few days away from work to process what's happening inside my mind and body and to just be with myself."

Ask for What You Need.

For instance, say to colleagues, "I'd like to take a few mental health days. I'll be away from my desk until next week. Please refrain from texting while I'm taking a break. I appreciate your concern but what I really need right now is quiet time. And thank you for holding down the fort while I'm away."

Follow through with the Requests from
Your Mind, Body, and Spirit.

"My body is asking for a long, quiet, phone-free walk through the park. I'll do that today."

Reflect and Register That This Was the Right Decision for You.

"I'm feeling a little calmer and steadier. I still feel grief, but it's more manageable now. Taking a break was the right call. Holy shit. This feels good. And empowering. I'm proud of myself for tuning into what I needed and giving it to myself."

When you continue this process—ask for what you need, reflect, and recognize that your choice was right for you—this is what builds self-trust.

Get clarity on what you want, need, and desire.

What's Something in Your Life That Depletes Your Energy?

You might be quick to mention "fertility issues," but go through other categories of life too. Is there a particular relationship, role, job, chore, commitment, or pattern that regularly depletes you? What is it?

Whatever it is, don't shame yourself for it. Uncovering this pain means there's an opportunity for more pleasure. Life will always be both a masterpiece and a work in progress.

What's Something in Your Life That Gives You Energy?

It could be your marriage, an old childhood movie, phone calls with your best friend, your morning routine, the time you spend swimming or jogging, or the happiness you feel when you declutter, clean, and adorn your home to make it feel like a beautiful sanctuary.

Can you receive the joy out of this thing?

Can you see your progress and note the areas of your life that ARE working?

What are some things you long for which you've been taught are invalid, wrong, or shameful?

What do you crave? What do you need more of? (And I'm not just talking about food!)

1. A simple yet life-altering question: *What do you actually want?* Are you structuring your life to fit in or get approval from your family, friends, colleagues, or work community? Are you following someone else's timeline or someone else's "ideal way" to a fulfilling life?

2. You are the highest authority on your life, mind, body, and fertility. Feel free to visit medical professionals, get opinions, and consider different plans. But always remember you get to decide the next right move. Just because someone urges you to do XYZ doesn't mean you have to. (While TTC, we sometimes forget this.) You always have a choice.

3. Take the baby off the pedestal. By attaching all of your joy, completeness, and purpose to your future baby ("Once I have a baby, then I will finally be happy..."), you're putting a lot of pressure on your body to perform in a certain way (and so much pressure on the spirit of your baby too.). No one person can be responsible for all of that.

4. When you want a baby with all your heart, and it hasn't happened yet, you may think, My hormones are betraying me, or I don't know what to think or do anymore. *I don't trust my instincts.* It takes practice to learn how to trust yourself again. One simple way to practice self-trust is to ask what your mind and body need ("I'm bored and need adventure!" or "I'm tired and need a nap!") and grant the request. See how this feels. This practice will remind you that your mind and body are speaking to you all the time, and they're giving instructions you can trust that lead to dreamy outcomes.

CHAPTER 5

SLOW DOWN TO SPEED UP

SAYING GOODBYE TO THE OLD YOU

The first couple years of my TTC journey, I should've earned an award for "Best Sufferer," complete with a golden trophy and an acceptance speech onstage. I was so committed to the idea and identity that having a baby requires discipline, sacrifice, and deprivation.

Over time, I gradually understood this suffering identity wasn't bringing my baby closer to me. To welcome a great life now—with or without a baby—I had to let go of the belief that suffering is necessary to get what I want and that it's the only pathway to success.

Looking back, I don't necessarily regret the years I spent suffering. From those experiences, I learned immense compassion for people going through hard things in life. Believe it or not, everyone has their "hard" in life. From addiction to divorce, hard is hard. And no one is exempt from this occurring at some point in their lives. Even that woman you know with three kids, the white picket fence, and the fancy-schmancy sports car.

I also discovered I wanted to live a life led by my nature, and I was so tired of getting distracted by victimhood, hustle, and force. If I was being really honest with myself, I became kind of addicted to the identity of someone who was "struggling to get pregnant."

When I felt ready to release my identity as a World Class Sufferer, here's what I did.

First, I grieved my old self. I wrote a letter to my Old Self, and I cried so many tears as I said goodbye to her. *Girl, did I cry!* I bid farewell to the part of me that identified as a poor, ashamed girl who wasn't able to conceive. I was genuinely sad to say goodbye to her. A loss is a loss. Even if what you're losing isn't serving you, the grief is real and justified. Even if I wasn't meant to conceive yet, I didn't want to limit myself to this circumstance anymore. I was fucking bigger than that. (And you are too.)

Next, I went outside on the deck at my family's lake house (which just so happens to be one of my favorite places in the whole world). I grabbed a pen and paper, and I connected with a higher power. I said, "If I'm not meant to suffer, then what? What am I meant to do?"

I got still. I made space. And I listened. In response, I heard this: "Spenser, you're meant to PLAY! To experience the world. To touch, taste, feel, smell, and take it all in! To explore what this life has to offer you. All the different landscapes. From water to winter. From happy to heavyhearted. To indulge in all the little things. To embrace and receive the big things. BE IN YOUR LIFE, BABE!"

I believe this is the promise of human life when we're in spirit form about to jump into our mother's body. "I want to go and explore! To feel it all. To grow into what I want to learn in this lifetime and feel what it's like to be alive!" That's how the spirit of your baby is feeling as you read these pages.

Being guided by this sage wisdom, I decided to make my life fertile ground for my baby. I promised myself, "Let me show myself and my baby how amazing life can be and feel."

Fertility wants to ask: You were not born to suffer. And if you weren't born to suffer, then what are you here to do? *What's left?*

Ask these critical questions, as I did. Get still. Make space. Listen for the answer. The answer may come to you in a whisper, almost as if someone is speaking to you, or in a passage from a book you underline three times, in a sign from nature, a bumper sticker, an oracle card or another clue.

SLOW DOWN TO COME BACK TO LIFE

Shortly after writing a sympathetic breakup letter to my former self, I landed on a book called *The Slow Down Diet: Eating for Pleasure, Energy, and Weight Loss* by Marc David. It never ceases to amaze me when a book presents itself at the right time. (Maybe this book, *Fertile Ground*, feels that way for you.)

The central premise of *The Slow Down Diet* is that the speed at which we eat (and do life) and the mindfulness with which we approach our meals have a profound impact on our digestion, metabolism, and overall health. The book argues that slowing down, savoring food, and paying attention to the pleasure of an eating experience can lead to better digestion, improved energy levels, and even weight loss.

Even though I wasn't trying to lose weight, I did want my body to feel safe and healthy without sacrificing the simple joys of life. I was so inspired by the book's message. Slowing down and adding vitamin P (pleasure!) into my life as a pathway to health and vitality? Ample research to prove that pleasure is not only nutritional, but an essential part of being alive? Sign me up. Remember, I had moved on from Ms. Spenser Sufferer. The Universe accepted my new truth and paved a new path by guiding me to this book.

Marc said, "Pleasure loves slow. It thrives in a warm, intimate, cozy space. It reveals its deepest secrets when we drop all pretensions of speed and allow timelessness and sensuality to breathe us back into each moment."

Marc believes the primary disease of our culture is speed, and the only cure is to slow down. (I couldn't agree more.) Because leading a hyper-speedy life dramatically impacts our autonomic nervous system.

The autonomic nervous system comprises two sections: the sympathetic nervous system and the parasympathetic nervous system.

THE SYMPATHETIC NERVOUS SYSTEM

This system is known as "fight or flight." It prepares the body for action in response to stress, danger, or excitement. When this system is activated, your blood pressure goes up, your pupils constrict, and your body quickly delivers oxygen to areas of your body, such as legs and arms so you can fight or flee from danger. When the sympathetic nervous system is activated, your brain tells your body, "Danger! We gotta get outta here! And BTW, this is not the time to get pregnant! We have other issues to deal with right now!"

THE PARASYMPATHETIC NERVOUS SYSTEM

This system is known as "rest and digest." It promotes relaxation and recovery. When this system is engaged, your heart rate slows, your blood pressure lowers, and your body secretes enzymes to help you digest food and turn it into energy. It's called the "feed and breed" system because, in women, it allows your body to secrete fluids that provide lubrication during sex. This system says, "You're safe, there's no threat here, you can rest and focus on tasks beyond survival."

When life feels like a frenzied rush to the finish line, this overstimulates your nervous system. Most people live their entire lives this way. Everything is always a rush—getting out the door for work, back-to-back meetings with no time to rest in between, cramming in one more email before leaving the office, stuffing their faces with a cold meal in front of the computer, dashing to the gym or back home, and frantically searching online to find a "five-minute quick and easy dinner idea." We constantly search for life hacks to do things faster. We groan with dismay when we have to wait for a few minutes on hold with a customer service representative or when a package will be delivered in one week instead of the same day. We want everything fast.

I realized how much I'd been rushing—during meal time and throughout my entire life. Rushing to get married. Rushing to buy a house. Rushing to get pregnant. Rushing to the "next best thing." Rushing toward the future life that my monkey mind repeatedly told me would make me finally feel enough. So much rushing, which undeniably over-activated my sympathetic nervous system, which then (ironically) put my body into a state that wasn't focused on conception. Trying to make things happen faster made all my efforts feel like they could move only in a teasing type of snail's-pace rate, intensifying all my impatience.

Moving too fast through life is like sprinting through a museum filled with priceless artwork. You might glimpse the vibrant colors and striking images, but you don't have a chance to truly appreciate the intricate details, the stories behind each piece, or the emotions they evoke.

I was so tired of missing out on the now. I was ready to live in a body and a life that felt safe to rest and be worthy of pleasure. I was so ready to recover from all the confusion, setbacks, and loss that I had been through up until this point.

As with any new endeavor, I didn't know if I could trust slowing down. I didn't exactly feel like I could afford to slow down. Hello! The biological clock was still ticking. Even though I knew there was evidence that slowing down could support my body to conceive, I was still skeptical. I coached myself through it by saying:

If you want to believe in a new outcome, you must believe in a new journey.

You can't keep doing the same thing and expecting different results.

If you're open to trying a new journey, all you can do is try.

You don't have to have 100 percent trust that slowing down will work. You can start with 5 percent trust and a willingness to just try. You can build more trust over time. It's okay to "date" an idea for a while and "marry" it later.

Plus, slowing down feels so damn good in the body. It feels lighter. Follow that feeling. Follow that knowing.

You'll notice that as I coach myself, I'm never invalidating how I feel. I'm never pushing myself to believe something that I don't. I'm always creating safety by compassionately validating any concerns, doubts, or worries. This tends to create an opening in my brain and body to begin to believe in something new.

So I gave it a shot. I did everything slowly. I picked my produce at the grocery store slower. I chopped my food slowly. I ate my food more slowly. I drank my coffee slower. I spoke slower. I made love slower. I walked in my neighborhood slower. I breathed slower. I bathed slower.

And the most remarkable thing happened...

Everything came to life.

The food tasted Michelin-star worthy. Sex felt like a powerful meditation. Sleep felt deeply restful. I was able to listen to the people in my life. The trees, flowers, and sky came to life with new colors and scents. Moving through this exquisite world, I felt like I'd never experienced such beauty before, but somehow, at the same time, remembered seeing and feeling that this is what life felt like when I was a child. Innocent, pure, in my body, and unencumbered by the societal pressure to rush.

It's exactly like one of my clients recently said: "The idea of slowing down didn't click for me. Then I started slowing down. And everything started to click."

One thing I remember, and it brings tears to my eyes as I type this out, is that slowing down brought my belly laugh. For most of my life, I thought I was destined to have a strange, silent laugh. How could other people have this big, beautiful belly laugh? Why was mine so quiet? Like a dry little chuckle, barely audible. Until one day, I let out a huge, loud, rambunctious belly laugh! I needed to slow down enough to bring this sound out of my body.

Slowing down also allowed me to make healthier choices without using willpower. Instead of following my old fertility plan, I aimed for more of a 75/25 rule. I ate mostly healthy foods (whole foods, unprocessed foods, and lots of fresh fruits and veggies) about 75 percent of the time because I want to have the energy to do the things I love. But I made space in my life for fun and freedom. I ate spaghetti and meatballs in slow bliss on Sunday family dinner nights, noticing every bite with every beautiful person beside me. I had permission to feel pleasure, guilt, and shame free!

Slowing down brought me back to life, and I believe it helped bring my two boys into my womb.

When we rush through life too quickly, our spirit babies struggle to find us. I imagine them calling out, "Mom! Slow down! Please! I'm trying to catch up, but you're going too fast." When we slow everything down, our babies have a chance to arrive.

THE MAGIC OF THE PRESENT MOMENT

Slowing down puts distance between you and your thoughts. And slowing down makes it much easier for you to connect with what your body wants and needs.

I remember this vision I had when I was working with a client. Her mind wasn't with her body. Her mind was ahead of her body. Ten feet ahead, always chasing the next shiny thing.

This depicts a mind and body disconnection perfectly. You need to slow down and come back into the body to connect the two. Come back to the part of you, the innate intelligence within your body, that has the answers to what you need.

You have tens of thousands of thoughts every day, but this doesn't mean they're true. Slowing things down creates space to ask yourself, "Do I even want to do that? How does it feel to believe this thought?"

For example, you get an email from that fertility expert about the newest, latest fertility fad or treatment. Immediately and impatiently, you have a thought. "I should do this. This could be the missing piece."

MIND-BODY MANTRA

Just because I have a thought *doesn't mean it's true.*

Self-trust comes with a level of discernment. The ability to discern what thoughts you want to carry in your mind and body and which thoughts you want to let go of. Give each thought space to see how true it feels to your body, not just your brain.

"My brain seems to think this is a good idea. How about you, body? What do you feel about this? I'd love to notice how it feels for you." And then slow down to see what sensations arise. Does your body feel heavy and tight? If so, it might not be the right next step. Does it feel lighter and more open? If this is the case, your body's signaling toward a yes.

When caught in the cultural rush, quickly moving from one task to another, it's nearly impossible to hear your body speak.

When I ask my brain and body for input, I've noticed that my brain tends to reply almost immediately, but my body needs more time to feel into things before responding. You see, although incredibly intelligent, the body does things slower. My brain is the quick-witted friend who always responds quickly, while my body is the more contemplative friend who needs a moment of silence to process before replying. Neither is good or bad, just different. But because our culture has such a strong preference for speed, the wisdom of the body often gets ignored. We've already rushed along to the next thing before she even has a chance to speak up.

When you're hypnotized by the false promise to get on the fast track to baby, or else you'll miss out on your window of opportunity, the only opportunity you're missing is the magic of the present moment. The opportunity to slow down, to question your default thoughts and actions, and to finally hear what your body has been trying to tell you all along.

THE GIFT OF TIME

Of course, time becomes a sticky topic when you're TTC. But it can be so eye-opening to explore, what "time" really is?

Put everything you've known about time so far aside and be open to seeing it from a more expanded awareness.

I don't believe time is as hardened as it appears to be from the surface. If you're willing to dive below the surface, like Einstein did, you might realize time is not as fixed as it appears but rather a dynamic and relative dimension.

Time is a function of memory. Memories glue the past and future together.

Time is also relative to the observer. Time expands or contracts, stalls or accelerates, depending on how you perceive things. It's actually pretty cool.

Imagine you're sitting in a restaurant, it's busy in there, the kitchen is slammed with orders, and it's taking thirty minutes for your dinner to arrive. You're sitting there alone, bored and hungry, and it feels like it's taking forever. Those thirty minutes feel like an eternity. Now imagine the exact same scenario, except maybe you're sitting across the table from your celebrity crush (Hey...blue-eyed Bradley Cooper!). Those thirty minutes would fly the hell by! Just the blink of an eye. You'd glance up in surprise as the waiter places your meal before you. "Oh wow! The food's here already!" Time is what you make it.

While waiting for your baby to arrive, you can speed through it and perceive the time as unbearably long. Or you can see that it's actually quite short in comparison to the entirety of your life.

Eckhart Tolle coined the terms "clock time" versus "psychological time." Clock time is used for the convenience of scheduling and showing up on time. Psychological time is our mental and emotional relationship to time. It's all the suffering we create around the perfectionistic timeline and expectations of how things are supposed to unfold by a particular (culturally set) time.

On my TTC journey, I remember many powerful moments when I let myself ponder my perception of time, as opposed to letting culture determine it for me.

One day, while walking around my neighborhood, I set an intention to connect with the energy of time and what it wanted me to know. Nearing the end of my walk, I had this visual of a map with many markings of adventure and all the things I came here to do in my lifetime. Time told me my life was so much bigger than this one circumstance of getting pregnant. The baby was a cherry on top! From this moment forward, time stopped feeling like a torturously slow goblin and more like an intelligence that was offering to give me more than I was even capable of asking for. We were now partners, working together to allow for my destiny to unfold. Time was no longer an enemy. Time had my back all along.

Time can be viewed as a collection of failures, disappointments, and unmet desires, or it can be perceived as an opportunity to grow into the woman and mama you are meant to be. Or a little bit of both. Time will exist either way, but how time feels and what you make it mean are up to you.

You may not get to decide how long it will take for you and your baby to meet physically because that part is not entirely up to you. But like my client Claire, you get to decide how it feels and if you want to partner with the intelligence of time.

CLAIRE'S STORY

I always wanted to be a mom. Some of my earliest childhood memories include playing house with my little sister. I was the mom, hiding dolls under my shirt to pop them out and rock them in my arms.

Fast-forward thirty years to a clinical IVF appointment and being told we had a 30 percent chance of a live birth of a child. I felt cold, shocked, and discouraged. I knew at that moment I needed to recruit support for the journey ahead.

Over the next two years, with the help of Spenser, we untangled a spaghetti pile of thoughts, fears, and attachments to outcomes. During one of our talks, Spenser said, "Tell me about your relationship with time."

That exploration sits with me still, as I lie next to my two-year-old daughter, lightly snoring with her feet snuggled into my side. Time was not against me on this journey, as I initially thought. Time was expansive and generous. Time was life enriching and life providing. It was a magical experience to bring my daughter into this world. Equally as extraordinary, I birthed a new version of myself. My own softening, unfolding, and grounding changed the way I live, love, and experience the world.

LESS EQUALS SO MUCH MORE

We've covered the importance of slowing down. You're now aware that you have sway over your relationship to time. And now, I'd love to demonstrate that doing less actually creates so much more.

Imagine planting a garden. Actually, scratch that. Imagine

overplanting a garden. Too many seeds are planted...everywhere. There isn't one inch of soil with space for the seeds to breathe. Why would one do this? Most likely due to a lack of trust in the seeds. Maybe they fear the seeds won't sprout, so better safe than sorry, right?

Not so fast. What happens when you overplant a garden? Well, a few things. The plants compete for resources, and this competition hinders growth. Limited airflow and close proximity between plants create favorable conditions for the spread of diseases. Over time, an overplanted garden can deplete the soil of essential nutrients more rapidly. Lastly (and I think we know this one all too well with the amount of shit on our fertility to-do lists), managing an overplanted garden soon becomes unmanageable.

Slowing your fertility journey down leads to more trust in doing less and with more presence. Naps replace overworking. Baths replace commutes to endless acupuncture appointments. Canceling plans replaces always saying yes in fear of letting others down. By slowing down, we naturally let go of all the distractions to stay busy that have piled up on the fertility journey. You begin to trust in a simpler life instead of feeling the need to complicate it.

I had an epiphany when I opened my fridge to make a smoothie one day. I saw all sorts of ingredients I could blend into my smoothie—bananas, apples, oranges, berries, spinach, coconut water, oat milk, flaxseed oil, chia seeds, nut butter...

Pulling everything out of the fridge felt exhausting. I thought about the mess it would make, and how much time it would take. And then, an aha moment appeared when I consciously decided to slow down before taking action.

I paused. I took a few deep breaths, and I heard a message from my mind and body: "Keep it simple. Choose three ingredients to put into this smoothie. That's all you need."

My smoothie epiphany showed me that I had a subconscious desire to make everything (even breakfast) harder than it needed to be. Why? Because in my mind, making it harder meant I would be more deserving of getting what I wanted. Except it didn't work like that. I was overcomplicating my life, my fertility journey, and my health. By simplifying and doing less, I signaled to myself, my body, and the Universe, "I'm inherently worthy of my baby. I don't need to prove anything to anybody anymore."

Complicating and constantly adding more keeps the narrative of "not good enough" or distrust alive and sends out a reactionary energetic signal that something is still wrong and you're not ready yet.

Remember, Mama Bear, you play the leading role in deciding when you're enough. If you're not hustling with complicated to-do's to prove your worth, then what's left? Presence. Freedom. Space to be in your life. Enough-ness is what's born.

I took a sip of my three-ingredient smoothie, and it was deliciously nourishing, sweet, and simple. Not too much or too little. Just enough.

If, no matter what you do, you never feel like you're doing enough, the result will reflect that. If you're doing less than you ever have, but you learn how to feel like you're doing enough, the result will reflect that.

You'll soon learn, just like Laura, that by slowing down, simplifying, and doing less, you are choosing to agree with how the Universe already sees you. Whole. Complete. Just exactly as you are.

LAURA'S STORY

In my quest to have a baby, I tried ALL the things: countless therapists, four naturopaths, three fertility clinics, and three years trying to get pregnant. I was meticulous about controlling my diet (no dairy, gluten, sugar, or alcohol) and exercise regime, and tried to create the perfect conditions to conceive.

My husband and I were literally the healthiest people I knew but somehow we had unexplained infertility. I couldn't understand why this was happening.

After two back-to-back miscarriages, I had the worst Christmas of my life (and I usually love Christmas). Multiple days in a row, I sobbed at my desk during lunch and had complete breakdowns on my kitchen floor. I was not coping. It was the hardest thing I've ever been through.

When I joined Spenser's program, I was at my lowest point. Honestly, I didn't think it would help me get pregnant. But I hoped it would help me grieve and heal from my miscarriages, find peace, and find myself again.

I joined the program in January. Then I switched clinics and did a second round of IVF in March, this time with twenty-two eggs retrieved, nineteen mature, eighteen fertilized, and zero embryos. You can't make this stuff up. Our doctor suggested considering a donor. To say we were shocked and devastated was an understatement.

I had a call with Spenser the night we found out. My husband said to me, through our tears, how grateful he was that I'd found a group of women who understood this particular kind of pain, who listened, and who cared. These friendships brought me comfort during a very tough time.

During a conversation with Spenser, I realized, "I have been gripping my fertility journey. My desire for a baby is so strong, I am shaking, I am literally choking the life out of it." She gently invited me to close my eyes, let go, and imagine myself falling. There was a beautiful soft cloud there to hold me. I didn't have to hold on so tightly. It wasn't all up to me anymore.

In the weeks that followed, I journaled and asked myself hard questions, the hardest of all being, "Who am I if I am not a mom?" Slowly, I released my grip and surrendered to the possibility that I may give birth, or I may not, and either way, I can have a fulfilling life.

I slowed down. I went for morning walks. I had long talks with my friend Susan, whom I met through the group. I felt more present with my husband, enjoying our life just as it is rather than constantly wishing things were different. On Friday nights, I soaked in my bathtub and listened to guided meditations.

We were going to do another round of IVF in June. In May, I had a dream in which my husband showed me our baby surrounded by ruby stones and purple smoke. I did a meditation and actually felt my baby curled up on my chest. I eased up on my food restrictions and treated myself to sparkling wine and pizza with real cheese! I stopped seeing my acupuncturist (their clinic was an hour away in Toronto) and instead of spending long hours in my car, I took more baths instead.

I was waiting for my period to come so we could start our next IVF round. It was late. I didn't think there was any possible way I could be pregnant. Not after everything we'd been through. Another week went by. Still no period. I had a few old tests in my bathroom. On June 1, I got a very positive test.

I wish I knew why the round of IVF in March didn't work and then why we got pregnant naturally in June. But no one will ever know. Pregnancy is a miracle that not even science can explain. What I do know is that desperately trying to get pregnant through control, restriction, and force didn't work. I believe that opening myself up, showing myself love, connecting to nature, God, and the Universe, looking for signs, and appreciating the beauty and wonder of life helped my baby find me.

THE TANGIBLE AND THE INTANGIBLE

Like it was for Laura, it might be hard to release your grip, or, more appropriately, expand your life's dreams beyond fertility, pregnancy, and motherhood. But there is no denying the power rooted inside of this one question: "What else do I want to gain from this experience, besides a baby?"

For example, perhaps you're considering a different food plan, treatment, new program, or protocol, and that's fine. If your body is asking for something new, honor that request and trust your decision. And then ask the following question: "What *else* do I want to learn from this experience?"

You create your main, more obvious tangible intention, but then create a second intention that is more of a feeling state you choose to expand into. By asking the question "What else?" you're not hanging your hat on one tangible outcome. You're allowing yourself to be open to all the ways, both tangible and intangible, that different inspired actions can enrich your life.

When I decided to do IVF, yes, of course, I wanted to get pregnant. But I also wanted to learn what it meant to surrender.

And so I told myself, "My number one intention from this experience is to get pregnant. I'm not going to deny that. My second intention is to learn more about what it means to surrender. To expand my capacity to tolerate the discomfort of not knowing."

Fertility challenges you to ask yourself, "What else do I choose to gain from this experience besides pregnancy?" This question helps you gain treasures from whatever experience you feel guided to move through. From this space, no matter what happens, it won't be for nothing. And this feels so soothing to the mind and body.

It's not about *what* you do, but *how* you do it.

You get to discover who you are beyond your reproductive journey, and you get to feel good while doing it.

While working on this book, I went to Hawaii on a writing retreat. One night, we went out for a leisurely meal at a luxurious hotel. I wore a long, hot-pink dress. A local musician played cover versions of pop songs on a ukulele. The sunset blazed fuchsia and orange in the sky. For three hours, we lingered over the decadent meal. Fresh salad greens and crisp crab cakes. Macaroni and cheese topped with lobster. Chocolate cake for dessert. I enjoyed a lychee martini (because, when in Hawaii...) and savored each sip. I left the table feeling awash with gratitude, went back to my hotel, slept deeply, woke up the next morning, and felt great.

Certain health experts might argue that mac 'n' cheese and vodka are not good for you. The worst thing you could possibly have! Sacrilegious in the self-help world. What a bad girl!

But I don't believe there's such a thing as good or bad food. Because if you believe a certain food is morally bad, then what do you believe about yourself if you were to eat it? More shame and more blame.

What I've come to understand is that (and this applies not

just to food, but to every part of life) it's not just about *what* you do, but *how* you do it.

Is the sex you're having to make a baby anything but sexy because you're just lying there wanting to get it over with? Or are you actually noticing the connection, the heat, the sensations between your physical bodies when you're making love?

Are you rushing your injections during your IVF treatment because you resent the fact that you even have to do it? Or do you take some time to register how brave and badass you are?

Are you rushing through your meals or savoring slowly? Do you eat in a peaceful setting or eat with vicious, fast-pedaling thoughts pounding through your head? Of course, not every night includes a gourmet meal in Hawaii, but when you're doing something special, do you say, "Wow, this is such a nice night, I'm so grateful to be here," or is it always, "This is sooo bad for me, I can't believe I'm doing this"?

Savoring cheesy pasta with friends while admiring the sunset is different from hurriedly stuffing pasta into your mouth in your kitchen, all alone, in a darkened room, except for the glow of the refrigerator light. You could have the exact same meal in both settings, but the research shows that your body processes the nutrients differently depending on your mental and emotional state.

Stress reduces blood flow to the digestive system and affects the absorption of nutrients in the gastrointestinal tract. This means you could eat the healthiest, most nutritious meal in the world—think: kale salad—but if you're in an anxious state, your body won't be able to absorb the nutrients optimally. Good health isn't just what's on your plate; it's what's in your head.

The same is true for alcohol. Western culture gravitates to binge drinking. Whereas in many European countries, there is a long history of responsible alcohol consumption as a part of social and cultural traditions. Drinking is integrated into meals, celebrations, and gatherings, emphasizing the importance of moderation and socializing. So is having a cocktail good for you or bad? Will it boost your fertility or derail it? Again, it's not so much about whether you choose to drink alcohol or not—it's how you feel about what's in your glass.

If you believe the glass of champagne you enjoyed at that celebration will erase your chances of getting pregnant, your body will react to these thoughts accordingly. Your sympathetic nervous system (fight or flight) will be activated, and your reproductive system might pause due to the perceived threat. Whereas if you enjoy the glass of champagne and decide that it's okay for you, your parasympathetic nervous system (rest and digest, feed and breed) will engage, putting your body into the optimal state for conception.

Am I saying you can do tons of meth, smoke a hundred packs of cigarettes, and finish it off with an entire tray of bacon, and as long as you think "nice thoughts" it's all good for you? Of course not. However, when you're applying discernment to your choices, your mind impacts your body a great deal. I trust you to know the difference.

Even the loathed rules of coffee in the fertility world are super subjective. While excessive coffee consumption can have negative effects, moderate coffee consumption is associated with several potential health benefits.

The big question is:

Does it feel good to your nature? If so, then it's the right choice for you.

Does it bring you satisfaction, presence, peace, inspiration, or energy?

If it makes you feel alive, more yourself, more present, then it's a healthy choice—and this applies to things like food, drinks, and exercise. But also to choices like the clothing you choose to wear, the people you surround yourself with, and the way you decorate your home.

Fertility wants you to know: I trust you to know what you want and need.

She trusts you to do whatever feels authentic, pleasurable, and life giving.

What turns you on, turns your fertility on.

This still runs true, even if you're about to do something scary like surgery, IUI, or IVF. Although the circumstance is not exactly desirable, you can still ask yourself: How can I make this scary thing more manageable, pleasurable, or personalized for my nature? Like my client Ashley F., you have a healthy sense of control over how you choose to prepare for this next step. Instead of applying physical force to an uncomfortable action and disassociating from the experience, you have full permission to create inner safety before doing it. And ultimately, it may lead to a surprising outcome.

ASHLEY F.'S STORY

IVF was something my husband and I never thought we'd do. There are so many reasons why. The main reason was we didn't want to play God. To us, IVF felt like forcing a child into the world—a child who didn't want to be here.

After meeting with an endocrinologist and going through all the tests, most of which were very painful, we felt even more lost. We were told, "IVF is your best chance of getting pregnant with a healthy baby." This felt like a punch in my stomach. I was sick about it.

On a call with Spenser and the other women in our group, I shared my feelings and received such compassion. Another woman had been through the IVF journey and graciously shared her story with me, explaining every detail of her experience. She told me, "There still has to be magic." Meaning, no matter how you get pregnant, whether naturally or with medication helping you along, there still has to be that magic moment when the sperm joins the egg. Nobody, not you, not doctors, can make this happen. It either happens or it doesn't. Right then, I realized if we tried IVF, we weren't forcing anything. The egg and sperm still have to decide to come together and create life. With IVF, or not, it's a miracle no matter what.

My husband and I talked it over for a full year, going through our thoughts and feelings about the whole process. As overwhelming as it was, these conversations brought us closer as a couple. Eventually, we decided to start IVF and felt excited! I never thought in a million years I'd be saying those words.

Moments after doing the first shot, I experienced a massive feeling of pride. "Holy cow, I just did that!" I felt so strong and brave. We were really going for it.

Everyone's IVF experience is unique, and each woman responds differently to the medication. For me, it was not as bad as I expected. Yes, by the end, I felt swollen, and tired, and had headaches and a few bruises. But I was not the hormonal monster I feared I would become. What helped the most was having strategies to de-stress and relax into the process. For some, this might be journaling or meditation. For me, it was cooking. I made a giant batch of my great-grandmother's soup, the most comforting soup I've ever had. I tried new cake and cookie recipes to share with my family. In the kitchen, I could focus on creating something wonderful, which is what my body was doing simultaneously.

At this moment, we've decided to hold off on doing our embryo transfer and instead do another retrieval. Instead of doing the retrieval right away, we're waiting a couple of months, because my husband wants to be home during the whole stretch and be with me every step of the way. When we decided to wait, I felt numerous emotions—gratitude for my sweet, caring husband and anger at facing yet another delay.

This whole journey is about waiting. To find peace, we have to change our relationship with time. Spenser reminded me that these little souls we want to bring into this world don't care about time the way we do. They're on their own timeline, whether frozen embryos or not. When she reminded me of this, something clicked. I realized, "This waiting period isn't another obstacle for me. It's an opportunity."

I have been given time to prepare my body for another retrieval, which I didn't get the first time around. I know what my body needs better than I did before. I know how my body will react to the medications. Most of all, I know I can give myself more grace through it all, no matter the outcome. Having extra time is a gift, and I will take advantage of it! I can enjoy my life now rather than waiting for my life to begin.

If this IVF process has taught me anything, it's "never say never." I never thought I could heal from our miscarriage. I never thought I would be able to stand up for myself and what I need for my health. I never thought I would do IVF. It's been an empowering process. My path is still long, winding, and full of potholes, but I know I am capable of handling whatever comes next.

Update: One month after Ashley F. sent me her story, she messaged me an update saying she is now pregnant naturally. She never thought she could get pregnant naturally. But here she is!

WHAT IS LIFE GIVING FOR YOU?

Like Ashley F.'s inspiration to cook her great-grandmother's heartwarming soup, what is life giving for you?

If something is nourishing for your soul, then it is nourishing for your mind and body connection, and ultimately for your fertility.

Make a list of things that feel nourishing and life giving for you, even if Western medicine doesn't agree with everything on your list. (Think: the cookies Ashley baked to enjoy and share with her family!) Maybe certain doctors or naturopaths would argue, "That's bad for you." Can you trust that it's life giving for you anyway? Can you discern by using the evidence you feel in your body, heart, and soul?

THE BEST YOU CAN

Even though you will learn what you need to feel good, I want you to know that there will unquestionably be days when you miss the mark. It happens to me all the time. It did on the fertility journey, and it does now as a busy mama of two boys while running a business, a home, and a happy marriage. It's inevitable. So expect it and learn that it's all about doing the best you can with your capacity today.

There will be days when you forget to drink enough water. Or you drink too much coffee preparing for a work project that you're super passionate about. Or you're tired from the red-eye you took home from your vacation. Or when your anxiety spikes out of nowhere because, I don't know...Mercury is in retrograde again. (Seriously, can't we blame the planets sometimes?) Instead of shaming yourself for not feeling perfect, positive, and high energy (all the damn time), offer yourself this forgiving thought: *I'm not feeling great right now. I took as best care of myself as I could as a human being in this body. I'm learning what I need and what I may have forgotten to give myself as I was caught up in the moment. Today, I'm going to meet myself exactly where I'm at, and give myself what I need.*

The goal is to do your best, not do things perfectly. Doing your best with your current capacity will absolutely fluctuate from day to day.

Fertility wants to remind you, "Your child isn't going to be robotically perfect. They're not going to operate at 100 percent peak excellence every day. Your kid will have amazing days, harder days, and all the other days in between too. You'll love them unconditionally through it all."

Can you offer yourself that same space? That same love?

MIND-BODY EXERCISE: DURING A QUIET MOMENT, ASK YOURSELF

1. Am I willing to let go of my identity as someone who has gotten really good at suffering?
2. What stories will I have to say goodbye to?
3. Letting go of an identity can be hard, even if it's an identity I no longer want. Can I let myself be sad about this loss? In other words, will I let myself grieve?
4. If I'm not here to suffer, then what am I here to do?

A Practice to Slow Down Your Life

What is one slow-down practice you can do to promote a more regulated nervous system and fill your life with more presence and pleasure? Here are some fantastic and super easy options:

Go for a slow-paced walk. Don't worry about getting your heart rate up, and take off your damn Fitbit if you have one of those monitoring devices. It's not about burning calories; it's about noticing the aliveness around you. Instead, receive the exchange of energy with nature, when you're not rushing to the finish line.

Make love in a slow and gentle motion. Tell your partner you want to take it slow. Set the tone and put on a sexy playlist. (Search Spotify. There are many. You're welcome in advance.) Become aware of the connection between you and your partner's body when you create space for slowness. What's it like when time isn't dominating the quality of one of life's greatest pleasures? Notice the temperature, the sounds, and the sensations. Does it feel more intimate? Maybe even more spiritual?

Totally savor a meal. Set the table. Light a candle. Take great pleasure in preparing one of your favorite meals. What's it like to believe there is no rush? Take one bite at a time. Chew your food. Actually be there in that moment, while you eat or even share a yummy meal. Take in each new flavor, texture, and color. What is it like to eat a meal with as much time as you please?

CHAPTER SUMMARY

1. "You were not born to suffer. And if you weren't born to suffer, then what are you here to do?" When you ask yourself this question, what answer do you hear in response?

2. Our culture is always calculating and rushing to the next best thing. We want to do everything better, harder, faster. But Fertility refuses to engage in this style of life. Less is so much more. She invites you to slow down, do less, and savor all the tiny "to-dos" in your life. As you do, you engage your parasympathetic nervous system, a.k.a. "rest and digest," or "feed and breed." When this system is activated, your body feels like it's now safe to conceive.

3. Conversely, when you're filling up your days with undesirable obligations, speeding at a frenzied pace, or continually telling yourself you're behind or not doing enough, this activates your sympathetic nervous system, a.k.a. "fight or flight." This signals to your body, "Whoa, we're in survival mode. This is not the best time to make a baby."

4. The irony is, when you slow down, trust the process, and notice all the gifts and opportunities that exist right now at this present moment in time, you'll (most likely) meet your baby faster.

5. Optimal health is different for every person. Sugar, carbs, dairy, alcohol, caffeine intake, certain forms of exercise, certain medications or vitamins—what feels great for one person may not feel the best for another. Rather than following someone else's plan, ask, "Does this feel good for my nature?" "Is this life giving for me?"

CHAPTER 6

MAKE PEACE WITH UNCERTAINTY

THE DISCOMFORT OF NOT KNOWING

I don't need to know when or how it's going to happen. I just need to know that someday it will.

That's the thought that ran laps in my head as I begged the Universe for immediate certainty to be okay.

Most women I work with are cool to wait for a baby, as long as they know what they're waiting for is going to someday (soon-ish) arrive. But it can cause so much anguish to let yourself be uncertain about your fertility journey. Like how and when it's going to happen. Or even if it ever will.

The question, "Will it happen?" is the most unsettling. It's the kind of monkey-mind misery that keeps you up at night in major frustration that you don't have more control, while simultaneously making you feel like you should have control.

You might be saying, "Spenser, this is the most uncertain

journey I've ever been on! How can you tell me I'm not willing to let it be uncertain?"

You'll get more clarity by learning you have two ways of responding to the discomfort of uncertainty that you face on the fertility journey.

One, you can accidentally refuse to tolerate uncertainty. You can try to push it away and out of your body by any means necessary. You can incessantly search for answers in an attempt to regain all the control (a.k.a. certainty) in your head. You can persevere in the constant teardown and reconstruction of your fertility journey. You can keep looking for all the answers outside of you. You can follow all the fertility rules you think you "should" do, even when you're exhausted and resentful. And the worst trap of all, you can keep believing, "When I get pregnant, that's when I'll fully live again."

Or alternatively, you can accept uncertainty's divine invitation.

Because that is what uncertainty really is—an invitation. Uncertainty invites you to learn something, to grow, to gain a skill or perspective you didn't have before. Initially, it's not necessarily a fun, sexy, or pleasant invitation, but it is an important one.

When I say you can accept this invitation, I'm not saying you need to accept the circumstance of not being pregnant yet. When I say accept, what I mean is bringing your life fully into this present moment. Accept the physical space you're in as you read this book. Accept the emotions and physical sensations that are currently streaming through your mind and body. Accept what is. Not forcing change or positivity, but letting this moment be as it wants to be right now. When you bring your attention inward, you notice that at this very moment, chances are...there are no immediate problems that exist right now.

This can create a new dialogue in your head. "Right now, at this very moment and in this physical space, everything's okay. I'm safe. Even amid the uncertainty in life. I don't have all the answers. But I don't need to have all the answers. *I'm not meant to.* Allowing this feeling of uncertainty to exist is part of the important work on the journey to my baby and a deeper relationship with myself. This is all that's being asked of me, right now."

HOW TO "DO" UNCERTAINTY

How do you make peace with uncertainty? How can anyone do this?

THE FIRST STAGE

Notice how you try to distract yourself or escape it.

Not in an attempt to self-shame, but in an awareness of how often you have an opportunity to drop back into the presence of your body, instead of the noise in your brain.

For example, there were so many times when I felt the tug of uncertainty during my two-week wait, and instead of leaning into it, I would quickly reject its invitation by grabbing my phone and manically start scrolling random fertility forums in an attempt to find other women who had similar symptoms as mine. Another example is the unrelenting need to pee on a stick and test (even though it's way too early to know) to avoid the discomfort of not knowing.

All of my clients agree that the last thing you feel after a frenzied Google search or testing too early is better or more relieved.

THE SECOND STAGE

Become familiar with what it's like to accept the discomfort of not knowing.

This can look like lying in your soft bed, closing your eyes, cozying up to the linens on your duvet, and silently repeating to yourself, "I feel so uncomfortable with not knowing, and that's okay. I accept this feeling of discomfort." From there, you can breathe into every part of your body, filling her with life, and perhaps gently ask your body if she's ready to speak to you. "Body, is there something you want to tell me about uncertainty? Is there a message you've been wanting me to hear?"

Because more often than not, this acceptance, underneath and through the discomfort, is a portal of so-fertile, so-alive, and so-prolific energy.

THE THIRD STAGE

Be patient with uncertainty. There is a gift waiting to be discovered as you walk through it.

When you believe you *need* to know all the answers, that creates an annoyed mind and a stomach-clenched pressure inside of your body that literally takes up every single ounce of your energy. There is no room for intuitive awareness, divine guidance, or new energy to enter into your mind and body, which actually and ironically leads to a calm feeling of spiritual-like certainty: an unexplainable knowing that all is well, no matter what happens, and that it's not all on you to control or figure it out.

I was invited to drop into this energy many times throughout those eight years trying to conceive, but I didn't have the skills or awareness to know how. I thought I was living in uncertainty, when in fact, I was doing everything in my power to keep it at arm's length. There's a major difference between reliving uncertain thoughts in your mind and embracing uncertainty in your body.

Above all, I didn't know that uncertainty held such a purpose for inner (and then eventually outer) transformation. Like Eckhart Tolle said, "Once you get the inside right, the outside falls into place."

Welcoming a new future seems like it should be easy, but like I've made clear, we're inclined to oppose the unfamiliar, even if it's what we've been wanting badly and potentially for years. The discomfort born from uncertainty is often the price of admission.

Uncertainty is a sacred invitation. A door opening. And through that door, you enter into a hallway. The initial emotion is a stinging discomfort, which is why most people refuse this initiation. If you continue to walk through, despite the internal conflict of, "I have no idea where this is heading, it feels odd, and I'm really unsure about this," you're gradually welcomed with a warm hug of calming energy. There's nothing to control or manipulate here. Uncertainty embeds its healing presence into your mind and body, reminding you that no matter what is going on in your life on the surface, you're being taken care of.

EXPLORING SENSATIONS

Clients often say, "I know that certain types of stress aren't good for my mind and body, so how can I determine what's the good kind of stress and what's not?"

Whether you use the word "stress," "intensity," or "sensation," you learn to discern by tuning into your body, because each experience feels different to her. Discomfort and pain are not bad for fertility and in fact can be powerful teachers. Suffering, on the other hand, is different. Suffering is not the ideal energy for fertility and, fortunately, it's optional.

Discomfort—Feels uncomfortable but bearable, might feel tingly, odd, unfamiliar, alien, like stretching your hamstrings at the end of a workout, that feeling of, "Whoa, that kinda hurts but in a clean way. I needed this." Discomfort can signal that you're stepping onto new terrain: "This is a place I haven't been before."

Pain—Pain can feel so many different ways: hot or cold, heavy or hollow, tight or piercing, frozen or shaky. When we allow ourselves to fully feel our pain, the intensity of the emotion usually rises and falls. It's a visitor that doesn't stay forever. Pain signals that you're a human being having a human experience in your body: "I'm hurting right now and that is okay."

Suffering—Suffering feels like a stuck-ness as you push against life. It's resistance to what is. It's what happens when we experience discomfort or pain and say, "I shouldn't feel this way," "I'm weak for feeling this way," "Something's wrong with me for feeling this way," and similar thoughts. Instead of simply allowing a sensation to be there, we judge it, we run from it, we ignore it, we deny it, or we try to numb it out. This causes the sensation to get stuck in our bodies and remain for longer than it needs to. Like a visitor trapped inside the house.

MIND-BODY MANTRA

As I allow the acceptance of uncertainty to settle into my body, I slowly and eventually experience a newly felt truth: that I can safely detach from anything outside of me needing to happen, and that I will still be okay.

When you're attached to the belief that you should have full certainty and control over certain aspects of your life, you don't recognize the truth that having full control isn't really something any human being would choose for themselves. On the surface, it sounds seductive. But in your mind and body, it would be far too much to bear.

It would be like being the conductor of an orchestra who insists on playing every instrument alone. While it might seem like ultimate mastery, the sheer beauty of music comes from the collaboration and harmony of different instruments and different musicians playing together. Not unlike the miracle of conception that comes forth from the collaboration of more than just you. This includes your partner, the soul of your baby, your body, the Universal plan, and every single person you choose to include on your fertility team. They are all part of the baby-making equation.

Fertility wants you to know: You are now free to make peace with uncertainty. You do not need to have all the answers. You are not meant to have all the answers. To do so would defeat the purpose of what life wants for you. Sit in uncertainty, and feel into what unexpected gifts are waiting for you to uncover.

Giving yourself permission to be uncertain and the ability to say "I don't know" is by all means serving a very high purpose in your life. It's teaching you how to allow your fertility journey to play its own unique symphony that's designed specifically for your evolution. Read Emily's story to see how making peace with uncertainty plays out in a real-life situation.

EMILY'S STORY

You've probably seen inspirational quotes that talk about "embracing uncertainty." Easier said than done. For me, learning to accept uncertainty was a big hurdle. Because, like many people, I wanted to feel certain and be in control of my future.

I learned over time, with a lot of guidance from Spenser, that I don't have control over many aspects of my life. So much of life is uncertain. You might be offered a job and get laid off. You could get married, and in twenty years, your partner might want a divorce. Very few things in life are guaranteed, and this isn't inherently bad. Uncertainty means the future isn't set in stone. Difficult things might happen. Wonderful things might happen too. Both can be true.

During one of our conversations, Spenser said, "Trust the discomfort of uncharted territory." I replied (somewhat frustrated), "Trust it to do what?" And she said, "Trust that it is purposeful." Something clicked for me at that moment. I didn't have to enjoy uncertainty; I didn't have to love it, but I could get my head around trusting that it was serving a purpose in my life. With patience and a lot of self-love, I could expand my capacity for uncertainty.

I realized, "I don't need to control my life so tightly. Control is an illusion, anyway." This revelation brought me relief. Instead of trying so hard to achieve and control certain things, I could just live.

I'm grateful I learned how to accept uncertainty before I started my IVF journey, which was one of the most vulnerable things I have ever experienced. When I found out my embryo transfer had resulted in a pregnancy, I entered a whole new level of uncertainty and vulnerability. I felt joy and relief but also fear and worry. I had to sit with the discomfort every day, knowing I didn't have control over whether the pregnancy would progress or what complications might arise. Again, I worked on finding relief in this lack of control, trusting the discomfort to be purposeful and knowing I could not control the outcome.

Learning to accept uncertainty has helped to prepare me for pregnancy, birth, and motherhood, which is arguably the most vulnerable experience of all.

As I sit writing this, I am thirty-three weeks pregnant. The uncertainty remains. The discomfort remains. We have had, and continue to have, many uncertain moments in this pregnancy. I feel both excited and scared to give birth, and I have learned how to allow space for both emotions and not to see either as good or bad, just human.

Every single day contains uncertainty. Instead of denying or fighting against this reality, I can hold it gently. This is life. It's hard and sweet, messy and simple, predictable in some ways and surprising in others. It's everything all at once. It has taken me a long time to realize this. And one day, I'll share these lessons with my child.

WHY DO YOU NEED TO KNOW?

How do you try to subconsciously distract yourself from feeling the discomfort (and acceptance) of uncertainty and not knowing?

Notice how your monkey mind strives for certainty:

"I just need to know if I'm going to get pregnant (and stay pregnant) or not."

"Is it going to happen this month? This year? Ever? By my birthday?"

"Is my baby coming? Or is this just not going to happen for me?"

When clients pose these questions, I compassionately reply, "Why do you need to know?"

Have you ever paused to consider this?

The reality is you don't need to know. You may want to know. The logical, analytical part of your brain will provide ample evidence of why you need certainty. But making it a need is untrue for your body. You don't need it. You need food, shelter, and water to survive. You don't need certainty.

Clawing for certainty is similar to grasping for perfection. You never reach it. It's not attainable. And it only creates unnecessary tension and suffering along the way.

If you ask your body and spirit, "When will it happen? Can you tell me, with certainty? Please?" they will reassure you that you don't need to know. That right now is enough.

A CONVERSATION WITH YOUR BODY

There's this moment stamped into my memory while TTC. I was having a bath, looking down at my naked body, and wondering, *What the heck is going on inside of here? What in the world is preventing pregnancy from happening? Why is this such a mind-fuck mystery? DO WHAT YOU'RE SUPPOSED TO DO!*

As much as I wanted to love my body and was told by society that I should love my body, I was confused by it and angry.

Then, I came across an IKEA commercial with an experiment of children in schools performing plant communication.

They were divided into two groups. One group of children was asked to speak rudely and loudly to one plant, and then the other group was asked to speak kindly and gently to the other plant. The plant that was abused became droopy and discolored. The nurtured plant was thriving, tall, and sprouting new leaves.

Seeing this experiment, I realized that my relationship with my body was very conditional and transactional. I praised her as long as she looked and behaved a certain way. But if she didn't do what I wanted, I bullied her.

I would only love and appreciate her if she could provide me with the illusory comfort of certainty and knowing.

Like the study's withering plant, my body could feel these conditional demands and my unconscious resistance to loving her.

I was missing the whole point. A mind and body connection is about establishing a mind and body relationship. You don't need to be a psychologist to know that any kind of human relationship does much better when there is unconditional love rather than a bunch of strings attached.

Although the physical body is a solid piece of tangible matter, it's made up of living energy. I'm not asking you to be nice to her so she'll do what you want her to do for you. I'm asking you to feel the delight of being a soul in a human body, to sense the energy inside of her in this incredible physical form. Beyond her appearance.

I needed to shift from "Do what I say, and then we can be friends," to "I'm sorry for how I've been treating you. Can we start over? I want to learn how to love you no matter what."

I rekindled my relationship with my body in quiet moments of meditation and even in long lineups at Costco. The way I'd acknowledge her and say, "Hi! How are you?" was by dropping my attention down to my body and beginning to notice my breath. I'd notice if there was any tightness anywhere, and then I'd bring my attention to that area of my body. It was miraculous when, almost instantaneously, any tightness would begin to dissipate with my presence and desire to connect.

I was building a new relationship with my body, and it wasn't based on performance anymore. I was no longer the employer (tyrant), and she was no longer the employee (victim). I didn't need outer validation for her to get pregnant to prove we were a team. I could feel, by just acknowledging her presence, that we were now working together. Not just to get pregnant but to enjoy this beautiful life together.

I imagine a conversation between you and your body. You ask, "When will you get pregnant?" And she says, "I don't know. I wish I could tell you, but I don't know right now, and I'm not meant to know. Do you think you can learn to love me anyway? Can we play in this life together, even though it's all a bit unknown? Could we try together?"

You take her hand and agree, "We can try."

This is one of the deep ironies of uncertainty. In the acceptance of letting things be unknown, *an inner aliveness rises up in your body*. Peace enters. It is so satisfying to give your soul permission to rest here. Almost as if this feeling—this resting place—is what you've been searching for all along.

DO WE NEED A BABY TO BE HAPPY?

One of the most impactful methods to make peace with uncertainty is through an open and honest conversation with the partner you're choosing to raise a child with.

It was Saturday morning. My husband, Dan, and I were having our weekly chat about how life is going. At this point in our lives, we had been TTC for over seven years. The first few years were full of shameful secrecy and suffering. But the later years were much gentler. We still had ups and downs, loss and grief, but we were much more accepting. We still wanted a baby, but it was no longer a feeling of desperate clawing. We wanted to get pregnant and stay pregnant, but we didn't want to rush the process and didn't want to make ourselves miserable getting there. We felt hopeful but patient, dancing with uncertainty a little more gracefully than before. We had officially taken the baby off the pedestal.

On this particular Saturday, we had never felt happier, more connected, and more free to do what we wanted. We loved our home. We felt blessed to live close to wonderful friends and family. We were going to concerts, fun dinners, and daily long walks with our two fur babies. On weekends, we drove to the lake to swim, party, and barbecue with my parents and siblings. Our sex life was, ahem, quite excellent. And our careers were thriving. My coaching practice was taking off, and I started a podcast that gave me so much joy. He made a career switch, too, and fulfilled his dream of becoming a financial advisor.

Rather than agonizing about how long it was taking to have a baby, we used the opportunity of extra time to focus on achieving exciting goals (that we would not have done if we'd gotten pregnant on our first try). We stopped following the life we thought we should be living, and were actually designing a life that we wanted. Life felt peaceful and harmonious.

Then it dawned on me. If we are happy now, then why did we need a baby to be happy?

"Babe, things are feeling so awesome in our lives right now," I said to Dan. "Of course it's not perfect; some days are tough. Unexpected shit still comes up. But we have more tools to handle it now. I know we would really love to have a child, but if we're happy now, clearly, we don't *need* one to live a happy life. We'd be okay if we didn't end up having kids."

Dan was rattled to hear me say this. After everything we had been through? We'd be okay *not* having kids? He's a planner by nature and has a clear vision of the future he wants us both to have. Waiting for kids he learned to tolerate, but no kids didn't fit the plan.

He excused himself and left the room for a moment to be alone with his thoughts. I gave him space. About half an hour later, he came back.

"It's really hard, strange, and even counterintuitive for me to admit this," he said, "but you're right. We don't need a baby to be happy, because we're happy now. Life is okay. Not just okay. Life is fantastic."

After this conversation, I felt a huge weight of pressure lift off my body. Like an elephant took its foot off my chest. I had no idea how strongly I had been holding in all of the pressure to provide a baby for my husband. As if it was all on me. He didn't put this pressure on me. Culture did. I did. And I was finally fucking free of it.

Shortly after, our baby boy Beck was conceived.

You've probably heard many people say, "We stopped trying so hard to have a baby, and then we got pregnant!"

Why does this happen? Partly because, as we've established throughout this book, your mental state has an impact on how safe your mind and body feel. New thoughts lead to new energy in the body, which leads to new outcomes.

And partly because it's the mystery of fertility that can't be explained. Maybe our spirit babies are watching what we do and feeling what we feel. Maybe Beck felt the shift just as I did, felt the pressure lifting from his own tiny chest. Maybe he knew, "My parents want me, but they don't need me. They're excited to meet me and they're already living their dream lives." And maybe this knowledge made him feel more secure to arrive.

Fertility wants you to know: When you remove the heavy pressure, that's when I can work my magic on you, and through you, with greater ease.

I'm thrilled to now introduce you to my hubby's side of the story. I see much significance and immeasurable relief in including your partner on the journey to conception—not in a controlling "do what I say" way, but more through leading by example. Here is a partner's perspective of the journey. Feel free to share his story with yours.

DAN'S STORY

As the male partner on the fertility journey, I felt helpless. I was always looking to fix the problem and any pain that Spense was feeling. Just like my wife, I was preoccupied with having a baby and had a long mental list continually running in my head of things to do and not do. I didn't ride a bike or go in a hot tub for years. Every time a microwave went on, I'd run into another room. Spenser and I spent copious amounts of time, money, and energy on the "next thing" that would supposedly help us get pregnant, because it gave us hope.

After a few years of trying to get pregnant, I noticed a change with Spenser. She needed less and less of my emotional support. Her coaching career taught her how to cope with the ups and downs, how to be okay with waiting, with loss, and with uncertainty. She wasn't always happy and still had tough days, but she seemed more at peace with the journey. Honestly, she was dealing with things much better than I was. So, reluctantly, I wanted to understand why.

I'm unsure if it's our society or my upbringing, but I don't feel comfortable talking about my feelings. When things get hard, I just go to work and do something productive to deal with pent-up energy and emotions. It's really hard to open up about challenges you're going through, especially with other males.

Spense introduced me to going within. Growing spiritually and emotionally. I read books written by other men, like Michael Singer and Tony Robbins, that had a blend of practical and emotional concepts that were easier for me to understand. I learned how to be more present. I even journaled and meditated. All things I had never tried.

There were some growing pains, but I found a routine that worked for me. Journaling was something I thought was only for women, but I tried it and enjoyed it. Just to tap in for a few minutes at the end of the day and off-load any shit I was feeling, and reflect on what worked. I noticed it also helped Spenser and I connect on a deeper level, and when we're in a good place, everything seems to be in a good place.

We were living a great life, other than this shadow of TTC. Spenser would always challenge me in conversations, but this time was a game changer. She asked me if I was happy, and when I said yes, she said, "Then why do we need a baby to be okay?"

I was taken aback at first, but this massive sense of relief eventually came over me. I started to question the story I told myself all those years ago, at the beginning of our journey, that we needed a child to have a real family and be complete. We would be okay if it was just the two of us.

As that realization settled into my body, something shifted in our lives. We decided to keep trying, but we were no longer attached. We enjoyed the things we "weren't allowed to do" for so long. I remember riding a bike and going in a hot tub the next week! Less focusing on what could happen and more on enjoying life right now.

You know our story by now. We have two amazing boys and are happy and busy chasing them around. Thinking that was all we needed was flat wrong. Kids are amazing, don't get me wrong, but they are a challenge. I'm so thankful for our journey and the life tools we learned because Spenser and I are closer than ever.

Looking back, and in my rookie attempt to give advice to any partners relating to what I have to say, the truth is you need to fail a few times and try a few different things before you're emotionally ready to accept there's a different way. A different way to think. A different way to feel. A different way to connect with your partner. And a different way to recreate the picture you originally had for your life.

The picture I had of my life was basic and boring, and this journey opened us up to so much more. In all areas of my life.

Spense has done an incredible job of condensing a decade's worth of time, energy, and money into a process, a book, and a program that works. But you have to be ready for it. And I think it's essential to be open to it as a partner.

Be open to trusting your partner. Open to being pushed out of your comfort zone. Open to listening rather than solving. Open to slowing down, reading, and even spending more time than you'd like talking about how you're both feeling because this is the least you can do to support her unending devotion to becoming a mother.

Your partner deserves it.

WORST-CASE SCENARIO ZEN

Although my heart told me Dan and I would one day have a baby, we had to accept what would happen if we didn't. Would we be okay?

The worst-case scenario while TTC is that you don't end up having a child.

If it triggers you to even read that sentence, I 100 percent get it. There were moments in my journey when that particular thought wasn't allowed to exist within my brain or within any brain near me. Because if it did, I could smell it.

Slowly and gradually, my thinking shifted from "I need a baby" to "I want a baby" to "I still want a baby, and in the meantime, my life is pretty great right now" to "If I don't end up having a child, I'll survive. I'll be okay. I *am* okay. I can have a happy, full, and abundant life with or without a child."

It doesn't need to take you this long, but it took me almost eight years before I could honestly say, "Baby or not, I can be happy either way." Eight years to recognize that my happiness is 10 percent dependent on my external circumstances and 90 percent dependent on my response to these circumstances.

Almost every time I got my period, I would default to the thought, *I somehow fucked it up again this month.* But then eventually I gave it back to the Universe, and I said, "You know what? I'm not making this about me anymore. I'm good now. I'm happy. I don't need to change anything. I'm ready when you are, but I'd rather live in the openhearted uncertainty of not knowing why it didn't work this month than the mean-girl certainty of blaming myself."

When I was finally pregnant after having a miscarriage, was I afraid of having another one? Absolutely. When my meticulously prepared home birth was switched to a C-section after finding out the baby was breech, was I scared? You betcha. When I got the courage to start my group coaching program, *Fertility Mind–Body Mastery*, was I worried it'd be a flop? Of course. But I knew I was safe even as those feelings crashed into me. I've learned that I can ride these waves of emotions, giving them space to swell inside of me and then depart like an ocean wave. I'll survive. I'll still be alive. I'll still like myself. I'm proud of myself for doing something scary. I know all I gotta do is to meet myself exactly where I'm at.

What I know for sure is I won't let the discomfort of uncertainty stop me from living out my dreams.

MIND-BODY PRACTICE: HAVE THE CONVERSATION

If and when you are ready, have a conversation with your partner to say, "We'll be okay even if we don't have a baby."

Again, and I can't emphasize this strongly enough, this conversation doesn't mean you're giving up on your dream. It doesn't mean you stop trying. It means you can continue to try but with a different attitude: "We're okay no matter what happens."

Continue to try but with even more trust in the unknown, with an open heart, with fewer rules and restrictions, with more focus on vulnerability and intimacy with yourself and with each other, with the deep knowing that you are okay right now, that your worthiness is not tied to your pregnancy status, and that a deeply satisfying life is not dependent on having a child.

This conversation might be hard. It could bring up unexpected emotions and maybe even some tears. It could also feel like an enormous release—like you're lifting a ten-thousand-pound weight off both of your shoulders. And this moment of long-awaited catharsis might be exactly what your mind and body need so very much.

Gentle Suggestions

Choose a moment when life feels good or great. Celebrate how many things seem to be working out, feeling better than they were before, and all the abundance that's showing up. Acknowledge that life feels pretty damn good as is, even without a baby.

Share one thing you've learned from this book with your partner. Perhaps you've had a realization about the difference between pain and suffering, about time, about uncertainty, or about something else.

Express (only if you actually believe it), "I think we could be happy even if we don't have a baby." If the word *happy* doesn't resonate with you, use different wording like, "We can have purpose and meaning," "We can have adventures together," or simply, "We'll be okay even if..."

Ask your partner, "Hearing me say this, how does that make you feel?" If they're not sure, or if they feel rattled and need some time to process, give them space.

You can let your partner know you still want to keep trying, but you want the journey to feel different than before. Describe a few changes you've already made or want to make. Maybe you want to slow everything down, or do something enjoyable (like taking a dancing class) instead of seeing doctors, specialists, acupuncturists, etc. numerous times a week. Ask your partner, "Is there anything you want to do differently too?"

PS: You might need to have the conversation privately with yourself, to process your own emotions, before you feel ready to talk with your partner.

CHAPTER SUMMARY

1. Uncertainty is an opportunity to learn something, to grow, to gain a skill or perspective you didn't have before. Initially, expanding your capacity for uncertainty doesn't feel great, but it's an undeniable opportunity nonetheless. Will you accept the invitation and see what's on the other side?

2. The only thing certain in life is uncertainty. Grasping for certainty is similar to grasping for perfection. You never reach it. It's not attainable. And it only creates unnecessary suffering.

3. You don't need all the answers along the way to your baby. Sometimes, the most liberating statement we can admit as human beings is, "I don't know. I don't need to know. I'm not *meant* to know." There is nothing that more quickly brings you into the accepted and magical state of the here and now than admitting you don't have all the answers.

4. Can you let go of the conditions you've put on your body? Are you able to partner with, accept, and maybe even love her now, regardless of your pregnancy status?

5. An impactful question: "Do we need a baby to be happy?" After eight years of TTC, I asked myself and my husband this question. We both surprised ourselves by realizing, "No, we don't." It's possible to desire something strongly and love your life as it is now. Both/and. Recognizing you don't "need" a baby can be so freeing and feel like an enormous weight has been lifted off your mind and body. Immense relief rather than so much pressure.

CHAPTER 7

THERE ARE INFINITE POSSIBILITIES

FROM A *NEED* TO A HAPPY AND HEALTHY DESIRE

When you make peace with not knowing and not needing to know, and realize that a happy-as-hell life is not dependent on circumstances going exactly how you planned but is much more dependent on your perception of yourself and the journey, then *you are free*.

Viktor Frankl was a Jewish psychologist who was imprisoned in a concentration camp by Nazis during World War II. In his memoir, *Man's Search for Meaning*, he describes the atrocities he experienced during WWII and the spiritual lessons he gained during his imprisonment. Frankl writes: "When we are no longer able to change a situation, we are challenged to change ourselves."

Please know that I'm not mentioning Viktor Frankl to minimize your pain. This is not me saying, "You know, infertility isn't so bad; it could be much worse; you could be a Jewish prisoner in WWII." My point here is that even when painful experiences happen, we have choices. And these current choices will shape our future.

As Frankl writes, "Forces beyond your control can take away everything you possess except one thing, your freedom to choose how you will respond to the situation."

You want a baby and don't have one *yet*. That's the life situation you find yourself in. Sure, you don't have complete certainty or control over this situation, but you get to choose how you respond. *Your response will influence both the journey and the outcome.*

Will you respond with resistance and annoyance and create unnecessary suffering? Or will you respond with curiosity? Will you respond by getting in touch with the intelligence inside of your body? Will you respond by developing a spiritual connection? Will you respond by slowing down? The responses you can choose are endless and exciting. Infinite possibilities.

There's a reason that I'm bringing up this topic of less control and more uncertainty near the end of the book. If I brought it up in the beginning, there's a good chance you would have slapped the book closed and not finished it. I know I definitely would have. But I'm mentioning it now because I trust that—by this point—you have enough evidence and openness to know that your fulfillment as a woman isn't created from your reproduction journey. When we know we don't need something outside of ourselves to be worthy, we feel more safe to let go.

Whether or not your life is one of quality is, and always will be, an inner individual journey. One that isn't dependent on another person, having offspring, millions of dollars, a bikini body, or life going exactly according to plan. Because it rarely does.

Some women fear that letting go of the need to get pregnant by exploring the possibility of not having kids will mean one of two things. One is that accepting this possibility means that no kids will definitely happen, due to a common but misconstrued Law of Attraction practice. (This is not the case.) Or two, that they'll have to plan what life would look like without children and start shaping their life around this. Switching their big home with bedrooms for a trendy apartment downtown. (This isn't true either.)

You can accept, "I want a baby. But I don't *need* a baby to be happy. I'll be okay either way" and still take action toward conception. Lots of great sex or intentional medical treatment can absolutely still occur. It just commences with a more compassionate presence, and it shifts the baby from a desperate need into a happy, healthy desire.

One of the main tenets of Zen Buddhism is that attachment is the source of suffering. The more rigidly we attach to a certain dream, the more suffering we create, and the more tension exists within the mind and body. Your work is to find a bit of wiggle room between you and the outcome. That's what psychologists and many spiritual traditions call "detachment."

Paradoxically, when you stop attaching your worth—your enough-ness—to your goals, the outcome begins to feel more doable and (my favorite) more pleasurable to pursue. You give the goal more space to joyfully unfold exactly as it's meant to and with less effort.

Fertility wants you to know: Instead of clutching onto your dream of a bouncing baby with a white-knuckling grip, squeezing so tightly that your hands are sore and turn red, release your grip. Just a little. Perhaps you can set that dream down gently. It can be in the same room with you, a few feet away. Still there. But now there's a little space between you and the dream. Don't think of it as letting the dream go, but as letting the dream breathe. Infusing it with new life.

THIS OR SOMETHING EVEN BETTER...

The only thing certain in life is uncertainty. And it will either be your ally or your enemy.

It's like, you go on a first date with someone and Uber home and wonder how it went. Will you go on a couple of dates and then fizzle out? Be together for a year or forever? You don't know.

You start trying for a baby and wonder when and how it will happen. Next month? Next year? Naturally or with the support of modern medicine?

You get pregnant and wonder what your pregnancy will be like. Is the baby happy? Will you get nauseous (like me) and eat only the saltiest of potato chips and sourest of candies for the first three months? Or will you be one of the lucky ones who gets to skim over that part?

You're almost reaching the end of your pregnancy. How will the baby arrive, and what will your labor experience be like? You finally bring your baby home and realize...how the hell are you gonna care for a newborn baby? Nobody can tell you exactly how it's going to play out.

You get my point. It's this inevitable thing that's there whether you like it or not. You don't know the answer to these questions. And *you're not meant to know.*

Believing you should have 100 percent control, full belief, and certainty that something will go exactly the way you want on your preplanned timeline leaves zero room for uncertainty. And in my opinion, uncertainty is more exciting than certainty.

Here's why: I have a human brain, which means I have limitations on what I can envision for myself. I always have an idea of what I want. I always have some dreams in play. (I'm a Sagittarius, after all.) But uncertainty means I'm leaving room for something bigger and better to happen. Something above and beyond what my little human mind can imagine at this point.

My small brain could not have predicted the rewarding career I inherited while TTC, in which I get to work with some of the most brilliant and dedicated women in the world. I could not have even imagined getting pregnant naturally two months after a failed FET. I could also not imagine being one of those women who says they "got pregnant unexpectedly" with their second child. And beyond these cocreations of tangible things, the fertility journey set a new standard for me in my life. I have a lifestyle I have fallen in love with. A slower pace I so appreciate. A husband who plays an equal role in parenting. A mind–body tool kit I refer to whenever life is feeling tight, and I need to drop deeper into my spiritual practice. A sense of compassion for days when I'm tired and need extra rest, which makes a world of difference in our culture hypnotized by hustle.

If you've been spending your energy believing that uncertainty is bad or intolerable, do yourself a favor and begin to build trust that the Universe knows what it's doing.

Here are a few mantras I love to use that root me in this truth:

MIND–BODY MANTRAS

Universe/God/Source, I choose this or something even better.

Everything is always working out for me,
even when it doesn't feel like it.

The best is yet to come.

You may have heard this famous quote from Albert Einstein: "The most important decision we can make is whether we believe we live in a friendly or hostile Universe."

Believe that the Universe is friendly, loving, understanding of how you feel, and wants the best for you and your soul's evolution. Which is why this book has landed on your lap. The Universe is not withholding from you. It's not teasing you. It's not testing you. It wants to show you how much it loves you.

Does this mean only good things happen? No. But remember, all the most challenging aspects of my life—the loss, the pain, the grief—have all been catalysts to a higher-quality life that I could never have conjured up all by my lonesome.

Imagine you're at a super taxing job. You haven't slept in days. Your armpits stink. You're almost passing out from hunger. You can't think clearly, and your eyes hurt from all the over-stimulation and fluorescent lights. But you can't stop because you've been under a spell that if you stop, then you won't get what you want.

Then imagine an overqualified, well-rested, fresh-smelling, cheery-eyed colleague stepping in to relieve you of this shift. "You go home. Get some rest. I got this!" she says. Mama Bear, this is what the Universe has been trying to offer you: rest, relief, restoration, and regeneration of your mind, body, and soul. Tag the Universe and focus on coming back to yourself.

It's true you won't know how your metaphorical workplace will run when you go home to take a hot, soapy shower, eat a turkey sandwich, and then pass out on your bed. But you can guarantee that everyone's better off.

UNCERTAINTY MEANS ANYTHING CAN HAPPEN

Letting life be uncertain holds the potential for *anything* to happen. Sure, uncertainty means something you don't want might happen. On the other side of the coin, uncertainty means your most significant, wildest dreams might come true. Uncertainty means you might end up with something so much better than whatever you originally planned. Uncertainty means infinite possibilities.

I find it helpful to know that our brains have a built-in negativity bias. We're wired to hyper-focus on the negative. That's why, when faced with uncertainty, we tend to focus on everything wrong that might happen rather than all the good that's more likely. We focus on what uncertainty might take from us rather than what it can give. But if the fertility journey has taught me anything, it's that life wants more for us, not less.

More trust. More feeling. More truth. More transcendence from the surface of life and into the fulfilling depths of our souls.

It takes intentional effort to counteract this negativity bias by consciously focusing on and savoring the goodness of life (despite inevitable challenges) to balance our perceptions.

Consider this scenario if it's difficult to imagine making peace with uncertainty. You're sitting down to watch a thrilling movie, popcorn in hand, and someone bursts into the room and tells you exactly how the movie ends. Ugh! You'd be so annoyed. "What? Why did you ruin it for me?" You didn't want to know the ending! You actually wanted the excitement of uncertainty! That's the whole point!

What if you applied this same perspective to your own life? "I'm on the edge of my seat to see what happens next!" "I don't need to know how it ends." "I can enjoy the journey of the story even if I don't know exactly where it's going." "I'm okay with being surprised."

As you accept and embrace the unknown, you learn more about what *life wants you* to know. What captivates me the most is that in exchange for the gradual release of the need for control over people and outcomes, you give birth to a profound sense of openhanded serenity. From here, you unexpectedly find yourself wielding slightly more sway over the unfolding of your life's path. Because when your well-being isn't contingent on external factors, you give way to a greater power, and there's no bigger force for creating a miracle.

Irrespective of your history, this still holds true. Even if, like my client Tammy, you've been through tragedy, discouraging doctor appointments, or failed IVF cycles yielding no embryos. Even if you think there's a limit to what the acceptance of not needing all the answers offers you, please read this story.

TAMMY'S STORY

As I write this, I'm sitting here with my eight-week-old, healthy baby boy. He is the joyful and miraculous result of a natural pregnancy after two and a half years of infertility, two failed IVF cycles, and being told I wouldn't get pregnant with my own eggs.

I had no idea that things would work out. I had a ton of evidence to the contrary. I tried all the things during my fertility journey—hundreds of dollars on supplements, hours of research, controlling my diet and exercise (and feeling guilty when I slipped up) and eliminating as many toxins from my life as possible. Nothing worked. Plus, my family was in the midst of turbulent times, including a major and shocking tragedy (my stepson was killed). Suffice it to say I did NOT feel positive or in control of my future during that time. My dream of having a baby felt out of reach, especially as I approached my fortieth birthday.

While working with Spenser, I realized I could never control the outcome and guarantee I'd get pregnant or that life would work out the way I wanted it to. At first, this frustrated me. Giving up that sense of control was scary, especially as a perfectionist and an achievement-oriented person. But the control was never real in the first place. It was only an illusion. My only real control was choosing whether to accept or fight against my circumstances.

I used to think terms like surrender and acceptance meant being happy even when bad things happen. However, now I think of surrender as simply receiving everything—not necessarily liking it, but without resistance or denial—including discomfort and uncertainty. Rather than forcing myself to feel positive, I accepted my anxiety. I focused on receiving and processing what was happening to me.

This practice is often clumsy for me. But over time, surrender allowed me to find a sense of safety in the moment. Not necessarily happiness at every turn, but moments of peace in the storm around me. It opened me up to receiving even more from the Universe.

Uncertainty holds not only my worst fears. Spenser taught me that it also has the possibility of magic and miracles. When the future is uncertain, anything can happen, including good things. I believe that surrendering during uncertainty helped me to be in a receptive state—which led me to receive my beautiful baby boy.

YOU DON'T NEED ALL THE ANSWERS

Tammy didn't have all the answers. I didn't have all the answers. Neither do you.

Being free from needing all the solutions to all of life's problems is precisely what roots you into the present moment.

Picture this: you're having dinner with a friend and they say, "Remember that actor from that one movie we saw together? You know, what's his name? He's tall, he's Canadian. Ugh, I just can't remember his name."

They describe the actor. You can picture him, but you're struggling to remember his name too. It's right at the tip of your tongue, but you can't quite recall. Allan something? Or was it Brian?

"Oh my God, this is going to drive me crazy!" you say, whipping out your phone. Not knowing is causing you to feel distressed, annoyed, itchy, and you're practically breaking out in hives. "Lemme Google it."

Nowadays, we are accustomed to having all the answers available 24/7 at our fingertips. We feel such discomfort with not knowing. Whether it's the name of an actor or something so much bigger, like when/if/how we're going to have a baby, we want a definitive answer *now*. When we don't have access to an answer, we say things like, "This is driving me insane!" "This is going to keep me up at night." Even when it's something as small and inconsequential as the name of an actor.

At first, it feels somewhat unnatural to realize, actually, *it's okay to not have all the answers*. It's okay to think, believe, and state with conviction, "I don't know," and "I don't need to know." It's okay to trust that life works out even if you don't know every detail of why, when, or how.

On my motherhood journey, there have been so many moments of uncertainty, not just during TTC but after having my babies too.

When I finally got pregnant after eight years of trying, I felt a whole new wave of uncertainty wash over me. Pregnancy after loss isn't easy. Plus, it was weird to be in the new identity of a pregnant person (imposter syndrome much?) after it didn't happen for so long. Even though I wanted to get pregnant more than anything, I didn't rejoice and do backflips when I saw those two pink lines. It took a while to breathe into this change, to accept that I wasn't going to know what the heck these next few months would look like.

There were so many moments when I had to let things feel hard—like the constant all-day nausea for the first three months and the anxiety I would feel before ultrasounds. Or when I had a spotting scare. Even though I was pregnant, uncertainty didn't disappear. If anything, it heightened because the stakes felt higher. Another reminder that circumstances don't provide relief.

My first son was born in March 2020, right when a worldwide pandemic was beginning. It was not easy, and I faced uncertainty around every corner. Would I have to wear a mask during labor? Would my husband be allowed in the room with me? Would we catch COVID-19 at the hospital? Could our parents visit us afterward? I had to remain rooted in my trust in the unknown. "This sucks, but I'll be okay even though I don't know what's going to happen."

In motherhood, I feel constant uncertainty. Now that I have two rambunctious, happy boys, who I'm so in love with, I have to trust the unknown more than ever before. I have to trust that other people are capable of caring for them so I can have time to myself. I must let go of being tempted to control every aspect of their lives because my monkey mind believes it's the only way they'll be safe. Although they're little right now, they are their own little souls. Accepting this truth requires constantly letting go of who I think they should be, and letting them be who they really are.

Imagine, again, that dinner with a friend. "What's that actor's name?" they ponder. But this time, you shrug. "I don't know!" Instead of whipping out your phone to find out—to try to relieve the discomfort of uncertainty—you keep your phone off. In this small moment, you expand your capacity to tolerate uncertainty.

You enjoy the rest of the meal. You share stories, laugh, and cry. You learn something new about your friend and about yourself as well. You split a slice of cake. As you hug tightly and say your goodbyes, you feel closer to your friend than before. The real gift is *you're in your body and present in the moment*—with all of its unknowns—instead of spending time in your head and out of the life-giving now, trying to search for certainty. As you're about to leave, it comes to you. "Oh ya! His name is..." And you both laugh and bond over how things eventually come to you when you choose to let loose and have some fun.

Fertility wants you to know: There are so many great mysteries—where we exist before we are born, where we go after we die, if we're alone in the galaxy, why pregnancy happens quickly for some and not for others. We may never know the answers to these questions. These questions are what make life interesting. Also, these questions make room for infinite possibilities. Even with all the unanswered questions, life is such a gift.

MIND–BODY EXERCISE: LIVING
WITH THE QUESTIONS

Max De Pree intended to become a doctor, but his studies were interrupted by WWII, when he served in the Army Medical Corps. His life took an unexpected turn after the war, and he became a business leader and author. He's known for saying, "We do not grow by knowing all of the answers, but rather by living with the questions."

What's one question you're living with, right now?

When you try to find a certain, definite answer to this question, what does that feel like in your body?

When you stop trying to find an answer, and simply allow this question to be there, with space, unanswered, what does that feel like in your body?

What if it is no longer your job or responsibility to find the answer or fix the problem? What does that feel like?

What if life wants to give you *more* than a baby?

CHAPTER SUMMARY

1. Uncertainty means infinite possibilities. Because the future is never certain, yes, this means something you don't want might happen. Conversely, uncertainty also means you could end up with something better than you could even imagine.

2. Choose to believe that we live in a friendly Universe. One that wants more for us, not less.

3. Uncertainty continues even when you get pregnant. It's there in conception, pregnancy, the birth of your child, and then in motherhood. Facing and feeling uncertainty is not defeat. It's exactly where you discover your inner strength and learn how to really surrender.

4. On your fertility journey, you have endless options. Whatever circumstances you find yourself in, you get to choose your response. Will you respond by letting go of your perfectionist tendencies and beginning to embrace your humanity? Will you respond by doing less and not more? There are many ways you can respond, but your ultimate decision should be tailored to your nature and will likely elicit a feeling of freedom.

CHAPTER 8

YOU ARE THE VESSEL

PERHAPS YOUR SOUL CHOSE THIS

We were in the jungle of Oahu, Hawaii. My husband and I embarked on a breathtakingly beautiful journey to a waterfall. We started off with a bright purple acai bowl in the parking lot next to all the local, lively chickens. Eventually, we made our way to the trail while passing wild cockatoos flying from branch to branch, singing their tunes in the tallest green jungle trees I've ever seen in my life.

I felt so alive. So unattached to needing anything more. I surprised myself when I felt inspired to ask the Universe, "Why is this fertility journey happening to me?"

Normally, when I asked this question in the past, the energy behind it was victimhood: "Why, God, *whyyyyyyy?*"

But this time, the question was born out of pure and completely detached curiosity. When I offered this question to the Universe on that day in Hawaii, I received an immediate reply: "You chose this!" The tone was kind and reassuring.

A few years earlier, this kind of response would have triggered the hell out of me. At a different point in my fertility story, I would have said, "Well, fuck you very much." But at this moment in my life, it felt right.

I chose to try to conceive a child. I chose to embark on this adventure. Nobody forced this upon me. By deciding, "I want to be a mom," I decided to walk down a path of never-ending uncertainty, mystery, difficulty, growth, and love. That was my choice. No one else's.

Some people believe we choose all of our challenges in life before we are born, and we arrive earthside with an assignment to complete—ordeals to move through, lessons to learn, strengths and gifts to share with others. Others believe that God/Universe chooses which challenges you get and never gives you more than you can handle. No matter what your belief system is, the concept of choice is empowering. "This was chosen for you." Or like the jungle trees whispered to me, "You chose this." Perhaps it's both. The Universe and I, "We chose this together."

Even though I had not yet conceived my baby—and even though I was on one of the most unexpected, complex, and honestly painful experiences a woman can possibly embark on in her life—it was paradoxically becoming, over and over again, the most fertile endeavor of my life.

I didn't choose the diagnosis of infertility. I chose the journey of fertility. There's a difference.

Eventually, I chose to trust the path that life was taking me on. I chose to not hate myself when my energy was unpredictably low, and all I could produce some days was enough energy to take a bath, lie in bed, and stare at the ceiling. I chose to trust myself enough to trust other people. I chose to trust that making my mental health a priority before having kids would make me a happy, well-nourished mother and wife.

Although I didn't have my baby yet, my life was *fertile as fuck*.

Not because I had more, but because I felt more. More in my heart, unapologetically and with compassion for my humanity. The definition of fertile is "producing abundantly." Fertile soil produces ample crops. A fertile woman produces so many things: thriving relationships, purposeful work in whatever form that may be, treasured memories shared with loved ones, wisdom to impart, unconditional love to share, babies, and more than babies.

The fertility journey can give you so much if you're willing to receive it.

For me, my fertility journey has provided the gift of remembering. Remembering where I came from and what I came here to do. It filled my life with so much purpose that I thought only a baby could bring. It created so much companionship and depth with my husband that I thought only a baby could create. And it brought me so much spiritual fulfillment that I thought only a baby could fulfill.

Along every unexpected twist and hidden turn that this fertility journey took me on, it was constant encouragement to drop deeper and deeper into the unknown, not needing to know exactly why it was all unfolding in this way, and letting go of things needing to look and feel perfect.

As I recognized the good already in my life and the satisfaction in the simplest of things—from how perfectly my head fell into my husband's shoulders as if our bodies were made and molded for each other, to the sound of my sweet West Highland terrier breathing her calm energy into my ear, to the small, warm sips of my morning coffee—these simple moments of life were all so satisfying. So satisfying I could finally let go and trust that life knew what it was doing.

Fertility wants you to know: You don't have to make it happen anymore. You can let go now. You can now be the vessel.

Julie's account vividly portrays the understanding that your life can be bountiful, vibrant, and purpose driven, even if you don't have your baby yet.

JULIE'S STORY

I was at my lowest point on my fertility journey, in a downward spiral trying to do all the things to improve my fertility, and nothing was working. I wasn't myself anymore. My husband and I weren't enjoying life like we used to, because I constantly wondered if the things we were eating or drinking were harming our fertility.

I took countless supplements (many of which I didn't even know how to pronounce or what they were for!), drank celery juice every morning (which I despised), did acupuncture and numerous other things. I followed what the experts told me would increase my fertility, even though I felt miserable doing it. All of this and I was still facing heartbreak month after month.

I was hesitant to join Spenser's program because I didn't believe that it could help me get pregnant. My husband encouraged me to sign up and said, "Even if this doesn't lead to a baby, it might help us get back to enjoying our life together."

Spenser often says, "Take the baby off the pedestal." If having a child is the absolute most important thing in your life, the only thing that matters, then you're setting yourself up for misery because you're grasping for something you can't control. This realization was a turning point for me.

I remember having a conversation with my husband and asking him, "Do you think we could be happy together if we never have children?" We both agreed we could. We loved our life together, we loved to travel, and we loved being an aunt and uncle. When he expressed, "Yes, we can have an incredible life no matter what," this was what my heart needed to hear. After that conversation, I stopped trying so hard to do everything perfectly for our fertility and slowly enjoyed my life again.

We began the IUI process while I was going through Spenser's program. The cycle when I got pregnant didn't make sense. The timing of everything seemed off. I questioned the team at the fertility clinic about the timing of scheduling the IUI. After the fact, I wondered if I had ruined that cycle by not listening to their suggested timing. But Spenser's coaching helped me realize that what I wanted mattered. I could trust myself and my needs. To my surprise, not only did that cycle lead to us getting pregnant, but we were pregnant with twins! When I finally gave up trying to control everything and started to ask for what I wanted—not from a place of control, but sovereignty—there was a greater plan waiting for me.

This journey did not happen the way I would have planned it. My time to become a mom came at the perfect moment for me and in the perfect way (even though at the time I often questioned it). I am forever grateful my fertility journey eventually led me to my babies. But even more than that, I have been so blessed by how it led me back to myself and made my marriage even stronger than it already was. My husband and I feel more equipped to tackle any other challenges life may throw at us because of this journey we've walked together.

SURRENDER TO WHAT WANTS TO BE BORN

Julie's journey depicts the clear difference between force and attraction.

Force is doing all the things.

Attraction is doing things for *you*, to open the channel to receive.

Martha Graham, the legendary dancer and choreographer, once described the creative process in this way: "There is only one of you in all time, this expression is unique, and if you block it, it will never exist through any other medium and be lost. The world will not have it. It is not your business to determine how good it is, not how it compares with other expressions. It is your business...to keep the channel open."

As Graham reminds us, you don't have to force anything to come out of you. All you need to do is keep the channel open. Keep your mind open, keep your heart open, and let the Universe use you to bring forth whatever you're meant to bring into this world.

This is another way of saying *be the vessel*.

As a vessel, the final outcome is not all on you. It's not your responsibility. You are the instrument. Somebody else is playing the song. The music comes from somewhere else and it flows through you.

You are a vessel during pregnancy. Your baby travels through you to get here. You borrow the energy of pregnancy for nine months and then you're not pregnant anymore. Your baby is here. Both of your lives continue on together, but also separately.

You are a vessel right now too. Knowing you are simply the vessel—and that you are not fully responsible for orchestrating everything else that has to come together for your baby to get here—takes the weight off of needing to make it happen.

Can you remember a time in your life when you felt like a

vessel? Maybe you got lost in a creative project and ideas started downloading into your head so quickly, as if the Universe was pouring the vision directly into you. After finishing the project, you felt like, "I didn't do this alone. I was the channel, and it came from somewhere else!"

Fertility offers you this truth: Being the vessel is not about achieving. It's not about figuring out how to do everything right according to what everyone else thinks you should do. It's about allowing the miracle to flow through you.

I am, and you are, a vessel.

A vessel for a higher power and plan.

A vessel for your baby.

A vessel for destiny.

You don't need to be a perfect vessel, but I believe you do need to be a trusting one.

Believing and feeling this truth is what allows your mind and body to soften, to relax the tightness to reach some unattainable, perfected state, regulate your nervous system, and strengthen your mind and body connection.

Have you ever seen a newborn baby sleeping? It is the picture of absolute peace. Every single muscle in their little body is completely relaxed. No tension. No gripping. So soft. To me, surrender feels like that. I imagine myself going limp as if I'm melting into the ground, and that's how surrender feels in my body.

You came into this world for a reason. You have an assignment to complete. You are here to birth something. It could be a baby. It could be more. Like something that has nothing to do with your uterus. Most likely, both.

What is asking to be born?

SURRENDER: A THOUSAND TINY MOMENTS

I wish I could provide you with this one pivotal moment in which I finally surrendered, but there wasn't one. To surrender is a compilation of a thousand tiny moments when you choose to trust instead of fight.

A few simple yet impactful examples follow.

Hannah was preparing for her IVF transfer and found out she needed to evacuate her house due to asbestos. She came to our group coaching call in a hotel room devastated that she wasn't able to fulfill the perfectionist fantasy of lounging in the comfort of her own home during her two-week wait. I encouraged her to surrender to it all. To let herself grieve what she thought it would look like. And also to comfort the depths of her vulnerability. To give herself exactly what she wanted, lots of time to just feel how she felt, lots of TV time, lots of room service, and lots of time to be alone. This might not be what everyone would want, but it's what Hannah did. She surrendered to herself.

Sherry found out she was pregnant and was terrified of loss. She was a grief counselor by career and had seen so much. She was petrified. When I see a client in a very heightened emotional state, I use guided visuals versus language, to get them out of the story of their heads and into their bodies. I took her (and the rest of the group) through a guided meditation, and I told her to imagine herself as a cheetah in the wild. I asked her what the cheetah wanted. She said, "To be around all the other cheetahs. I want to feel surrounded and comforted by other animals." This was Sherry's message from her spirit and what she needed to feel safe. Unlike Hannah, who craved quiet alone time, Sherry wanted to be engulfed in the love of other people. Allowing herself to create that space was an act of surrender.

Nicole was asked if she wanted to have a laparoscopy procedure to explore what might be occurring underneath her diagnosis of unexplained infertility. She was a health coach and felt shame for needing any kind of procedures or assistance to help her get pregnant. One of her acts of surrender came from deciding to do this procedure to dismantle the shame she had around asking for help. We are all worthy of support. Everyone needs help in some area of their lives.

Katherine, a big-time lawyer who was literally trained to bypass her energy and emotions in order to be successful at work, slowly began to thaw her body and feel how she really felt. Even if it was highly uncomfortable, she believes that every time she felt a real, true, authentic emotion, she surrendered more deeply into what wanted to move through and out of her to make space for her baby.

Rebecca felt so incredibly uncomfortable when a family member offered to pay for her dinner. She grew up having to raise her young siblings and not relying on anyone financially from a very young age, so it felt like too much to receive. Reluctantly, she graciously accepted it as an act of reception and surrender.

Emma, who took such pride in a perfectly put-together Martha Stewart–worthy home, let her house get a little messy. Especially when she came home from running her own business and was living off the reserves of her energy. I asked her to let her house look lived in. Essentially, to let her house become a home that would soon be filled with the messiness of a child. This was a practice of surrendering to her humanity.

All these examples are of women not adding more to their mental to-do list, but accepting what is already there, underneath cultures' incessant call to achieve more. When all the noise is quieted, they can finally hear their souls speak.

Through Annie's story that follows, it becomes even more

evident that surrender often hinges on a slow embrace of your imperfect identity, a loving acknowledgment of your basic needs, and the recognition of your innate worthiness for a great life, exactly as you are now.

ANNIE'S STORY

When my husband and I decided it was time to try to conceive another baby, I assumed it would all run smoothly. Why wouldn't it? We had already experienced a miscarriage before my daughter and I truly thought I couldn't be so unlucky to have another. Well, we did. I tried my best to act like I wasn't bothered and that we would just try again. As if it was just another day and a month gone by.

I tried to convince myself I was completely fine. However, my body showed me so many signs that I had not fully grieved my second loss. My mood was all over the place. I couldn't sleep, my heart felt like it was in a constant rush, and I found myself talking really negatively toward my body and what I thought it hadn't done for me.

I wished so much to be a different type of person, to be the carefree person who wasn't fazed by life's challenges. Fast-forward four months after my second miscarriage and I found myself gripping onto anything to conceive again, to make everything feel right in our family.

While working with Spenser, I thought what I would get out of it was a baby, but what I actually got was a love for myself. A kind of love I truly hadn't felt since I was a little girl. (And eventually, I'm grateful to say that I did get pregnant halfway through the program, but not through forcing or temperature tracking!)

The biggest and most relieving change has been the way I talk to myself and show myself love in times when I need it the most. I'm talking about those times when I've felt anxious and scared, while TTC and now while pregnant.

Another huge part for me has been asking the Universe for signs. I didn't grow up religious, which never bothered me. But when I began to see the signs I asked the Universe for, it really built my trust that everything was going to be okay for me, baby or not.

I have let go of so many controlling tendencies, trying to force things around me to work out perfectly. I used to make sure everyone else's needs were attended to before my own, just so I knew I had done enough before I would enjoy anything myself.

I remember this moment before getting pregnant with baby number two when my husband, my two-year-old, and I went on a night walk in our local botanical gardens. They had put up beautiful displays of lights and sculptures along with music. Usually, I would preplan a toddler dinner, snacks, and bath time, and make sure she has enough sleep that day, preparing for every possible scenario down to the most minute detail. But after working with Spenser, I chose to just let happen what will.

My toddler had maybe five hot chips for dinner (that's French fries for those in North America), refused to go in her pram, and wanted to be carried after the halfway point and it began raining! But I honestly felt so at peace that night despite the imperfections. I enjoyed every moment of the lights and the walk in nature, and I felt so connected and loving toward myself. It was a night I won't ever forget. My second child was conceived not too long after that evening.

I can't say I have gotten the carefree personality I've always wished for, but what I have gained is such a love and appreciation for the person I am.

The person who cares so deeply about others. The person who is meticulous and puts time into things and relationships that matter. The person who, now, can embrace the beauty of imperfection. The mama of two who is more than enough.

A GREAT GARDEN OF OPPORTUNITY

Surrender is a progression. A choice to consult with your mind and your body every day. A choice to cocreate your life with the Universe, partnering together rather than you alone attempting to run the show. A choice to decide that just because life isn't going according to your initial plan, it *doesn't mean it's not working out.*

Let's bring it back to the metaphor of a garden. If you've ever planted one, you know that so much devotion and attention is given to both the soil and the seeds when you plant them. You carefully space the seeds out and into (what you hope is) fertile ground. You prepare the soil as best you can, knowing there is no such thing as perfect soil. It doesn't need to be perfect to produce a delicious, generous crop. Planting is full of playful impatience as you anticipate and envision an abundant garden. Awaiting the day when you will finally bear the fruit of your love to a thing that isn't even really a thing yet. Your imagination runs wild with different recipes you'll soon create with your fresh harvest.

A couple of days pass and you wonder, *What's taking so long?* You keep watering and weeding. Nothing seems to be sprouting yet. *Is anything even happening? I can't see anything yet!* you wonder. Eventually, you get back to your life. Staring at your garden until it grows would be a waste of time and honestly boring as hell. The ground needs space to receive energy from all the other sources of life that aren't in your control, and simultaneously, you trust the sun will rise every day. Plus, the other adventures of your life are calling you.

Then before you know it (and this is what it feels like every summer for me), your garden is overflowing with a variety of lush produce. A full bounty for you to enjoy and share with everyone you love. Almost too much to know what to do with.

Just like the fertility journey is for me, all of my clients, and you, the seeds we *get* to plant on this journey are more than babies.

They're blooming businesses. They're thriving marriages. They're new homes. They're vulnerable conversations. They're long-awaited vacations. They're days off to do nothing or anything. They're puppy adoptions. They're sincere relationships with yourself. They're spiritual practices.

Some seeds come up faster than others. Some take their time. Some need tending to and more thinning to make more space to grow and eventually spring through.

So many of the women I work with have gardens that are overflowing with beautiful bounty, but they're focusing on the one seed that hasn't sprouted yet.

As much as you desire to create an ideal environment and fertile ground for a baby, it's not up to the gardener. It's up to the seed when it's ready to arrive.

Your garden is a vessel for these small but mighty seeds of possibility. The only thing you can do is tend to the garden as best you can, nourish it, give it space and time, and trust it will all unfold as it's meant to.

TRUST IS NOT CONDITIONAL

In terms of trust, I'd like to focus on *real* trust.

While I was in my first trimester of pregnancy with my second baby, a client asked me, "How do you trust that everything's gonna work out?"

"I don't know if it's gonna work out," I responded. "And I still trust."

I continued, "My trust isn't dependent on the result of conception and pregnancy or the result of going full term and having a baby. That's in the hands of a higher power, and it's up to my baby's spirit. And I trust my baby will do what's best for them. I'm just the vessel. I can't hold all of that responsibility anymore."

Trust is not conditional on things 100 percent going your way.

Trust is about believing that even if things don't go according to your plan and your timing, things are still—and always—working out. There's always a bigger plan. Always magic being curated behind the scenes, even when on the surface, things feel hard, painful, and confusing.

You don't have to orchestrate everything. Even in loss. Even in failures. Even in the will-this-ever-fucking-happen and not-again moments.

If we trust life only when things are working out—or in other words, if we're trusting only perfection—then we never really learn how to trust life. Because life is not perfect.

We must let go to make room for the magic and the beauty that is asking to be made.

Fertility wants you to know: Trust the journey of this life. Trust that life is working in your favor. The more you trust the journey, the more fluid and joyful your life becomes.

MIND–BODY EXERCISE: ASK FOR A SIGN

One way to establish trust and make room for more magic in your life is to ask for a sign.

Asking and receiving signs on the path to your baby is the most exciting and enjoyable exercise out there. It provides excellent comfort to the mind and body that it's safe to relax, and it fills you up with so much trust that shit is going down behind the scenes in the best way possible. Best of all, it helps you to believe in magic. The magic it takes to make a baby.

Here's what I want you to know before asking for a sign.

But What if It's Just a Coincidence?

Perhaps it is. Maybe the thousands of signs that my clients, podcast listeners, and I receive that continue to guide us to huge joy and lots of babies, and then more joy, are just random coincidences. For example, I asked for a ladybug sign in the dead of winter. I never thought I would see it, but my nature told me to ask for it. That week, I dropped my son off at school on Halloween, and his teacher welcomed him head to toe dressed as a...you guessed it, ladybug. *She was even wearing ladybug earrings.* Maybe it is a coincidence. We get to meet our analytical minds with, "I don't know for sure." However, it feels so much more flippin' fun to believe that unexplainable magic is at play. And how you feel is important.

Signs Will Always Fill You with Peace.

Remember, the Universe is a friendly Universe. Look for feelings of lightness in your body to validate the appearance of a real sign. I don't believe there are bad signs to warn you of danger. If you think something is a sign, but it's making you feel more anxious, then it's not a sign. It's just anxiety.

More than Anything, Signs Appear to Assure You That You're on the Right Path.

Some people make the mistake of receiving a sign and then immediately jumping into the analytics of their brain and asking, "OMG, what does it mean?" Signs don't arrive to provide you with more control. They arrive to let you know you're on the right path and you can let go of control. Signs provide relief that you're in the flow and validate the decisions you're making. Your only job is to receive the gift of guidance.

Ask for One Sign at a Time.

Keep it simple. Less is so much more. Think of one sign you want to see to let you know you're on the right path to your baby.

Here are some examples: A song you love. An animal. A feather. A coin. A flower. A number. Even a color.

You can write it down in your journal. And then, let it go. Get out and enjoy your life. Let the Universe get to work with zero effort on your part.

1. Fertility is not just about making babies. Although you might not have your baby yet, your life can be fertile as fuck. Not because you have more but because you feel more. More in your heart, unapologetically and with compassion for your humanity.

2. What does it feel like for your body to be the vessel? It is not your responsibility to fulfill the spirit of your baby's life from start to finish or to calculate every single action to make it happen. You are the vessel. Surrender to something bigger than you, working through you.

3. Surrender is a progression. A choice to consult with your mind and your body every day. A choice to cocreate your life with the Universe, partnering together rather than you alone attempting to run the show.

4. Trust is not conditional on things going exactly according to your plan. Can you trust that your life knows what it is doing?

5. You came into this world for a reason. You have an assignment to complete. You are here to birth something extraordinary. What is asking to be born? Baby and more?

CHAPTER 9

YOUR VERY OWN MESSAGE FROM FERTILITY

Fertility has one more message for you:

What is it, Mama Bear?

It is now time, and these pages are space to have your very own conversation with Fertility.

One of my grandest intentions for you on the journey to your baby is to hear your own voice. To be connected to your very own internal compass. You now get to practice being your own authority in your life.

Get still. Breathe. Don't overthink it. And then write:

Dear (Your Name) _____,

This is Fertility. And here is my message for you...

....

....

CONCLUSION

Mama Bear, if this book somehow landed into your hands, I believe something beautiful is meant to come through you. Something more than you could ever imagine. There's a bigger plan waiting for you if you allow yourself to melt into it.

The energy inside this book is more than a recipe for increased fertility. It's the recipe for living a life according to your unique nature. You can copy and paste everything you've learned into every category of your life. The best part is you will pass this encoded energy down to your future child.

SUMMARY OF THIS BOOK

We've covered so much together. Hundreds of pages. Dozens of stories from women on their fertility journeys. So many concepts that I've invited you to breathe in, hold gently, consider, and integrate into your life.

I want to leave you with a summary of everything we've discussed. All of the biggest gems from this book are summed up in one place.

If this summary speaks to you, take a photo of these next few pages and keep them on your phone, or underline certain sentences that feel like exactly what you need to know...or have always known.

More than anything else, this is what Fertility wants you to remember:

YOUR MIND AND BODY ARE DESIGNED TO WORK TOGETHER

The research shows that your thoughts, beliefs, and emotions impact your physical body. There's a direct connection. What's happening in your head will either activate your sympathetic nervous system (fight or flight, not great for baby-making) or parasympathetic (feed and breed, ideal state for conception).

This is great news because you can harness the mind–body connection to your advantage. You can use mind–body medicine to increase fertility, and you can use it to alleviate suffering and improve the overall quality of your life in every category of your life. A win-win situation.

It's also important to accept that there is a mysterious aspect to the fertility journey. There are many questions unanswered and unexplained by even the world's top fertility doctors. Conception is truly a miracle and when overanalyzed, it loses its mysterious and magical essence that is an essential ingredient to its active existence.

THERE IS ANOTHER WAY

The journey to your baby doesn't have to feel like deprivation and sacrifice. It doesn't have to include rigid rules, protocols, and diets that strip every ounce of pleasure from your life. It doesn't have to be a full-time job. If you've tried that type of approach and it's gotten you nowhere, you have full permission to stop.

Especially when you're in the grips of hustling for your worth and trying to "do more in order to have more." If what you're doing isn't working, don't do it harder.

You can move toward your baby in a different way. You have full permission to cut your to-do list in half, ask for help, and receive all the love in your life right now, even before your baby arrives.

There is another way to meet your baby, and it's softer, gentler, and more connected to your unique nature.

FEEL THE FULL SPECTRUM OF EMOTION

You don't need to do, eat, say, and think everything perfectly in order to get pregnant. Perfection is not possible. Stop playing that lame-ass game and instead meet yourself where you're at. Allow yourself to feel *all* of your feelings inside of your body. Your wholeness and finally feeling "enough" includes your imperfections.

The more you are ashamed of how you're really feeling, the more the natural emotions get stuck in your body, which turns healthy, clean pain into unnecessary suffering.

People often say, "Just relax, and then you'll get pregnant." A better way to say this is, "Relax into the truth of whatever you feel in this moment, whether it's hope, excitement, anticipation, grief, sadness, or anger."

Every emotion just wants to be heard, seen, and acknowledged, not resisted or judged.

MEET YOURSELF AGAIN

As you've been trying to conceive, you may have drifted further and further away from your true nature due to social pressure and a desire to fit in. You look at your home, career, or marriage and wonder when things became so unaligned, stagnant, and colorless.

When did I stop doing what I wanted to do? What happened here? Who am I?

You have an opportunity now to let go of the shame that's piled up and meet yourself again—much like reconnecting with an old friend you haven't seen in a while. An opportunity to remember, *What do I need, if I didn't feel bad needing it? What gives me energy? Who am I besides a woman who is TTC?*

While waiting for your baby, you can use this time to come home to yourself, to your nature, not the "you" that society has conditioned you to be.

There is a powerful woman inside of you, and she is fertile as fuck. Now. Not just when you get pregnant.

SLOW DOWN TO SPEED UP

Rushing activates our sympathetic nervous system: fight or flight. When this system is engaged, your brain signals to your organs: "We have an imminent threat in our midst. Do whatever is necessary to survive. But, this is probably not the best time to get pregnant."

Slowing down engages the parasympathetic nervous system: rest and digest, otherwise known as feed and breed. Food gets digested better and converted into energy, oxygenated blood flows to your reproductive organs, and your body settles into the optimal state to conceive.

Slow down every part of your life—the way you eat, the way

you make love, the way you process your emotions, and the way you navigate your fertility journey. Ironically, slowing down allows you to create what you want faster.

You may be in a rush to meet your baby, but remember that the spirit of your baby doesn't comprehend time the same way you do. For your baby, there is no rush, no late or early, only divine timing.

MAKE PEACE WITH UNCERTAINTY

The only thing certain in life is uncertainty. Yet we waste so much energy fighting against this truth. We want things to be guaranteed, and in our quest for certainty, we cause ourselves so much unnecessary anguish.

The more we expand our capacity to feel the initial discomfort of uncertainty, the more content and trust we feel. But you won't know this until you try it.

You'll face uncertainty while TTC, while pregnant, during labor, as a mother, and in parts of life that have nothing to do with parenting. The sooner you can make uncertainty your ally, the better.

Include your partner in this process to help take the pressure off. Ask each other, "Will we be okay without a baby?"

THERE ARE INFINITE POSSIBILITIES

How you choose to respond to uncertain times in life has an effect on the outcomes in your life.

Will you respond with curiosity? Will you respond with more self-compassion by understanding that you don't need all the answers? Will you respond with more trust that something bigger is unfolding behind the scenes?

Uncertainty is a two-sided coin. Uncertainty means hard things might happen. But it also means your wildest dreams might come true, or even something bigger and better than whatever you originally dreamed.

YOU ARE THE VESSEL

When and how you have a baby is not entirely up to you. You are simply the vessel.

Let go of the gripping, the force, and the intense pressure because the final outcome is not your responsibility.

Being a vessel is the ultimate act of trust. Trust that even if things don't go according to your plan...things are still working out. That there's always a bigger plan. That something miraculous and mystical is being born even if you can't see it yet.

Something wants to flow through you and into the world. Besides a baby, what else is asking to be born?

YOUR VERY OWN MESSAGE FROM FERTILITY

It's time to become your own authority in the journey to your baby. What message does Fertility have for you? Trust what you receive, Mama Bear. It will not lead you astray. You are wiser than you give yourself credit for.

DO YOU SENSE HER?

Perhaps you are starting to embody the essence of Fertility. You're slowly and subtly beginning to understand what she's been trying to tell you. You'll know if this is true if you feel even just 10 percent more relief in your mind and body than you did when you first began reading this book. If so, please note the progress.

As you can see and feel, Fertility is very different from all the numbers, diets, and statistics culture sadly diminishes her down to.

She, like you, is so much deeper than that. So much beyond the appearance.

She is not here just to support you in getting pregnant but to be that creative force necessary to conceive all of your gifts and move through life with groundedness and safety. She is the ever-present feminine energy that runs through your blood.

THE PROGRESSION OF YOU

Change never happens all at once. It's a progression. I've made it very clear in this book that you'll face moments of resistance along the journey. Things will start feeling better, but then your monkey mind says, "It's too good to be true," or "This feels too easy." (According to mainstream culture, success must require grinding, sacrifice, and suffering.)

I invite you to notice what has changed for you since opening this book for the first time. What progress do you sense in your mind, body, and spirit?

Note if you are feeling more supported now. More trusting of life at this moment. More understanding of what it *really* means to surrender. More willing to feel the feelings you haven't let yourself feel in the past. Better equipped to stop referencing your past to reaffirm you are not allowed to feel safe today. More of a healthier sense of control over how you choose to respond to your life. My greatest wish is that you feel more relief and free to live from your nature.

Acknowledge the progress you've made along your fertility journey, because if you don't celebrate these victories, then it's like they never happened.

What's right about your life?

What do you want to celebrate right now, and how do you want to celebrate it?

What does it feel like in your body to stop resisting who you really are?

Can you let your life feel okay, good, even great...even if your baby has not arrived physically yet?

ABOVE ALL, REMEMBER THIS

If you remember nothing else, remember this: When you will find yourself most accepting of the present moment—even if you don't have everything you want right now—and when you will find yourself most able to take in and explore your current life, is when you stop the fantasy that eventually, you will be perfect. And that this is the only qualification to finally being enough.

You will never be perfect. And yet, still wildly worthy, insanely valuable, and lovable—beyond your mind and body comprehension.

You'll never be the perfect wife, the perfect vessel for your baby, or the perfect mother, because perfection does not exist. It's a target you'll never hit. However, this actually doesn't matter because you don't need to be perfect to have what you want. It's no longer a qualification for entry to your ideal life. You can be imperfect and have a totally awesome marriage, a super satisfying career, a home filled with laughter, a rambunctious family, and more. Isn't that such a relief? To know that perfection is not a requirement for the life that you want? Hallelujah!

Fertility wants you to know: You're the one you've been waiting for. You are the only one who can embrace and embody the wholeness of who you are. Your wildly productive days when everything feels flowy and effortless. And the days when you need to curl up in bed and watch your favorite rom-com to soothe your sorrow. Your nutritious grilled veggie and salmon nights and your frozen pizza nights. All of it. Let all these parts of you exist, just as you'll let the fullness of your future child exist. They will be a complicated, messy, wonderfully imperfect human being *who is already enough* just like you.

All the acceptance, compassion, generosity, and tenderness that you'll one day bring to your baby, Mama Bear, give it all to yourself.

You were brought to earth for a purpose. You will birth many things in your lifetime, not only a baby. You are already, always will be, and always have been *Fertile Ground.*

ADDITIONAL SUPPORT

As you reach the end of this book, you may think, *I love all these new concepts! This feels so right. But now, what do I do?*

Let your intuition guide you. What feels right? What is your body asking for?

Here are a few options to consider...

WORK WITH THIS BOOK

Reread certain parts of the book. Sometimes, a message will sink in deeper when you read it a second or third time.

Throughout the book, you'll notice questions to consider. Grab your journal and take the time to answer those.

Take time to rest and digest too. You may want to take a break from thinking about this book and return to it a week or two later.

Remember, your fertility journey is not a school project. There's no right or wrong time frame. Do what you feel inspired to do. Some weeks, that might be more, and some weeks, that might be less. It all depends on the seasons of your life. Listening to what you need and giving it to yourself (without guilt) is part of how you connect with the energy of fertility.

LISTEN TO THE *FERTILE GROUND* PODCAST

Search for *Fertile Ground* on Spotify, Apple Music, Stitcher, or wherever you get your shows. I release new episodes regularly. Listen on your commute to work, while taking a lovely nature walk, getting ready for the day, or anywhere you want.

Sometimes, I interview clients on my podcast, and they share their fertility stories. Other times, I talk about aspects of the fertility journey that I believe need more love and attention. I hope this podcast feels like curling up in a comfy chair with a friend who really *gets* you.

WORK WITH ME

I invite you to check out my website to learn how you can work with me at http://www.spenserbrassard.com.

Or you can apply to join my group coaching program, Fertility *Mind-Body Mastery*. You'll find the application at https://www.fertilitymindbodymastery.com. Many of the women who contributed stories to this book are program graduates (and I'm so grateful for each person who generously allowed me to include her words in this book).

My programs allow you to apply everything you've learned in this book to your fertility journey. Because it's one thing to read about connecting with the energy of fertility—slowing down, releasing perfectionism, embracing uncertainty—and it's another thing to get your brain coached and feel that shift in your body.

Some women join my programs because they're TTC and want to try a different approach. Many join because they sense, "I don't want to do this alone anymore. I want to make this easier. I'm worthy of support. I need people I can talk to. I need women in my life who *get it* because they're going through it too. I need a space where I can receive guidance when I'm confused, and where it's okay to cry and be a complete mess on hard days. I also want to remember to celebrate how far I've come instead of always searching for what's wrong."

Clients describe my coaching style as similar to a big sister who fiercely protects and loves you, and who also lovingly calls you out on your bullshit, revealing who you already are right now. Whole and complete. As is.

SAY HELLO ON SOCIAL MEDIA

Honestly, I would love to hear from you! I'd love to hear about your fertility story, where you're at, and how you're feeling. Send a DM to @spenserbrassard on Instagram.

Whatever you decide to do next, if it feels right, then it is right. You know the way.

ACKNOWLEDGMENTS

They say it takes a village to raise a child, and it certainly takes a village to birth a book. So many people helped to make this book possible. I want to thank...

My husband, Dan, who gave me the kick in the ass I needed to write this book. Not only did you graciously give me unwavering support through all the weird TTC shit we did, but now, you're watching our boys and giving me all the free time I need to write and get this book out to the world. It means the world to me. I love you. You're my safe space. So honored to be on this journey of life with you.

My kids, who were the dangling carrot I needed to actually commit to this inner work. Beck, you're wild, full of joy, so sure of who you are and what you want, and you like to do things on your own time, without force. It makes sense why you took so long to come here. The lessons you gave me in those eight years, I can't ever repay you for. I'll do my best. Jack, you couldn't wait to jump into this crazy family. We're so happy you did. Your kind eyes and huge smile add so much love to our family. Thank you to my children for shaping me into the most nourished mama *before you even arrived.*

My parents, for raising a woman who saw life's challenges and made them life's gifts. And to *our whole family*, I know you didn't know exactly how hard this journey was for Dan and me, but we never once felt judged or less than because we didn't yet have kids. Thank you for your acceptance of exactly who we are.

My clients, who make me laugh and cry every week, who inspire me with their courage and willingness to grow, and who said, "Yes!" when I asked, "Would you share your story and allow me to publish it so other women can see it too?" I did this with you. You are part of this book. You are changing people's lives with your vulnerability and strength.

My writing coach, Alex, your calm, feminine energy is exactly what I needed to stay in my body and in my heart while birthing this book. It set the tone for such ease. The tears we shared while forming this book will be locked in my memory forever, as well as that delicious lobster mac and cheese dinner.

Lastly, the energy of Fertility. I love working alongside you. I'm so honored to be your conduit. I'm mostly grateful, though, for your full acceptance and permission for us women to be messy, naughty, human, and free.

I don't know exactly how this book will be received by the public. I don't know if it will sell ten copies or one hundred or ten million. I don't need to know, and I'm not meant to know. I'm just the vessel. I also know this book won't be "perfect" either. Not perfect *and* still enough. Just like me.

ABOUT THE AUTHOR

SPENSER BRASSARD is the host of the top-rated podcast *Fertile Ground*, which has over five hundred thousand downloads, and the author of this book.

She's the creator of *Fertility Mind–Body Mastery*, a program that shows women how to harness the power of the mind–body connection to get happy and pregnant.

Harvard researchers have found that when women use the mind–body connection and have emotional support from a circle of women, this increases the likelihood of conceiving by 55 percent. Spenser brings this evidence-backed method to her clients.

Spenser's work and programs include coaching and community support for women as they ride the highs and lows of the TTC journey. Clients call the program "life-changing" and "the greatest gift you can give yourself."

After working with Spenser, 70 percent of women get pregnant within one year after working with her. The 30 percent who aren't pregnant (yet) experience a shift in perspective and feel more peace, patience, and trust in the process.

Spenser is a certified Life Coach trained by Martha Beck, who is best known for being Oprah Winfrey's personal coach. While navigating her own fertility journey (eight years of trying to conceive), Spenser felt a strong pull to work with TTC women and help mamas find their babies. For her, coaching is more than a career. It's a calling.

She's been married to the love of her life for thirteen years, and they're raising their two boys.

Learn more about her work at www.SpenserBrassard.com.

NOTES

1   World Health Organization, "1 in 6 People Globally Affected by Infertility:
     WHO," press release, April 4, 2023, https://www.who.int/news/
     item/04-04-2023-1-in-6-people-globally-affected-by-infertility.

2   Alice D. Domar, "Impact of Psychological Factors on Dropout Rates in Insured Infertility
     Patients," *Fertility and Sterility* 81, no. 2 (February 2004): 271–73, https://doi.org/10.1016/j.
     fertnstert.2003.08.013.

3   Amy F. T. Arnsten, "Stress Signalling Pathways that Impair Prefrontal Cortex Structure
     and Function," *Nature Reviews Neuroscience* 10, no. 6 (June 2009): 410–22, https://doi.
     org/10.1038%2Fnrn2648.

4   Alice D. Domar, Machelle M. Seibel, and Herbert Benson, "The Mind/Body Program for
     Infertility: A New Behavioral Treatment Approach for Women with Infertility," *Fertility and
     Sterility* 53, no. 2 (February 1990): 246–49, https://doi.org/10.1016/S0015-0282(16)53275-0.

5   Silvia Schneider Fox, "Mind-Body Program," Fertility Resilience, accessed February 27, 2024,
     https://fertilityresilience.com/mind-body-fertility/.

6   Alice D. Domar et al., "Impact of a Group Mind/Body Intervention on Pregnancy Rates in
     IVF Patients," *Fertility and Sterility* 95, no. 7 (June 2011): 2269–73, https://doi.org/10.1016/j.
     fertnstert.2011.03.046.

7   Alix Spiegel, "Mind over Milkshake: How Your Thoughts Fool Your Stomach," NPR,
     April 14, 2014, https://www.npr.org/sections/health-shots/2014/04/14/299179468/
     mind-over-milkshake-how-your-thoughts-fool-your-stomach.

8   Craig Marker, "What Housekeepers Can Teach Us about Weight Loss," Breaking
     Muscle, last modified November 22, 2021, https://breakingmuscle.com/
     what-housekeepers-can-teach-us-about-weight-loss/.

9   Todd Smith, "What Exactly Is the Work of Byron Katie and 4 Questions?," The Work
     as Meditation, accessed February 27, 2024, https://www.theworkasmeditation.com/
     the-work-of-byron-katie-4-questions/.

10 Lisa Miller, *The Awakened Brain* (New York: Random House, 2021), 150.

11 Kristin L. Rooney and Alice D. Domar, "The Relationship between Stress and Infertility," *Dialogues in Clinical Neuroscience* 20, no. 1 (2018): 41–47, https://doi.org/10.31887/DCNS.2018.20.1/klrooney.

12 American Psychological Association, "Manage Stress: Strengthen Your Support Network," last modified October 21, 2022, https://www.apa.org/topics/stress/manage-social-support.

13 Paul H. Grunberg et al., "Infertility Patients' Need and Preferences for Online Peer Support," *Reproductive Biomedicine and Society Online* (August 2018): 80–89, https://www.ncbi.nlm.nih.gov/pmc/articles/PMC6282097/.

14 Dr. Alice Domar, website home page, accessed February 27, 2024, https://dralicedomar.com.

15 Candice Georgiadis, "Women in Wellness: Dr. Alice Domar on the Five Lifestyle Tweaks That Will Help Support People's Journey Towards Better Wellbeing," *Authority Magazine,* November 26, 2021, https://medium.com/authority-magazine/genwrightwomen-in-wellness-alice-domar-on-the-five-lifestyle-tweaks-that-will-help-support-4969e38fd27.

16 "The Wizard of Oz: Pay No Attention," Grant Lewis, December 31, 2007, YouTube video, 1:50, https://www.youtube.com/watch?v=NZR64EF3OpA. Here's the link to let this one sink deeper into your body.

17 Elizabeth Perry, "How Self-Compassion and Motivation Will Help Achieve Your Goals," *BetterUp* (blog), September 19, 2022, https://www.betterup.com/blog/self-compassion-and-motivation.

MEDICAL DISCLAIMER

This book does not replace the advice of a medical professional. The reader should consult a physician in matters relating to his/ her health and particularly with respect to any symptoms that may require diagnosis or medical attention. The use of this book implies your acceptance of this disclaimer.

Made in the USA
Coppell, TX
17 March 2025

47220996R10142